FOR PARTIES

FOR TRAIN RIDES   FOR CONVALESCENTS

TO KEEP YOUR MIND SHARP

TO KEEP THE KIDS BUSY

FOR THE JUST PLAIN LAZY
(AND THE CRAZY)

WHEREVER YOU ARE
WHATEVER YOU ARE DOING
WHOEVER YOU ARE

Here it is—a *brand new* book of fun and excitement for everyone in the family. Bridge puzzles, literary tests, memory tricks—for insomniacs, train riders, lone wolves. Fortune telling, a murder game, "ice-breakers" to make *your* party a success. Even doodles by famous people! See what Ginger Rogers does with a wiggly line! See how much fun you can have with these 166 pages of new quizzes, puzzles and hilarious games!

PUZZLES

QUIZZES

and GAMES

By Phyllis Fraser
and Edith Young

BANTAM BOOKS
New York

A BANTAM BOOK
Published February, 1947

Printed in the United States of America

FOREWORD

For many years we have had a hitherto-useless talent for solving any and all kinds of puzzles. Too often we have been the instigators of parlor games at parties which were in no way our own responsibility. This has caused some friends to label us little Elsa Maxwells. Our husbands, who have had to supply definitions or play games when they were seriously involved in men's talk, have understandably called us names less flattering. Our hope is that this book may prove to those long-suffering gents that solving puzzles and playing games all these years have proven to be a valuable apprenticeship.

To increase our own list of puzzles and games we have plagued our friends and searched through volumes in the public library. No trunks were left unopened, no attics unexplored. Radio quiz programs have been dinned into our ears, and our eyes have burned scrutinizing periodicals with game and puzzle pages. We have invented a few puzzles, but all the puzzles and quizzes are new in the sense that we have worked out entirely new problems and answers. You will not have worked any of them before, since this is not an anthology, but a brand-new collection.

Authors of puzzle books, like ourselves, actually originate very few puzzle forms. Most games and puzzles go back to antiquity, to early Egyptian and Roman days. It is practically impossible to create a puzzle without ancestors. This, however, does not detract in any way from the fun of working the puzzles and playing the games.

In the course of our research for this volume it was interesting to note how many times certain puzzles sprang up in other collectors' books with claims of originality. Only minor changes had been made—either consciously or unconsciously—in the puzzles taken from classic sources. Quite often the changes were an improvement on the older versions, and for this reason we believe the practice is legitimate. A specific example of a change for the better is the card trick which we use in our Ice Breaker Section (see page 97). The trick was originally worked with four Latin words as the key. Some considerate, laborious soul, whose identity is unknown to us, found four English words with the necessary repetitions of letters to make it a simpler trick for those of us who know no Latin.

We have not tried to create any parlor games in this book, but have served only as reporters of the better games we ourselves have played. Nor are there any changes in "Fortune Telling With Cards," which appears in the Ice Breaker Section (see page 106), as we are not seeresses, and are not qualified to elaborate on the subject. We merely feel that it is an important aid to any hostess entertaining guests who like to hear themselves talked about. So we included it. It is to be borne in mind, however, that this game is offered only as a "conversation piece" rather than a serious augury which might change the course of anyone's life.

We have tried to include the widest variety of puzzles and games, so that everyone may find a particular favorite. We have purposely omitted crossword puzzles, since they are available in most daily newspapers and in many books. Omitting them has simply given us space for newer types of puzzles which, we hope, will appease the crossword-puzzle fiend.

If this book affords you amusement, fills a lonely moment, or helps to make a party gayer, it accomplishes what was intended.

Phyllis Fraser
Edith Young

FEBRUARY, 1947

CONTENTS

II. QUIZZES

III. ICE BREAKERS

IV. PARLOR GAMES

V. PARENTS' TREASURY

Paper & Pencil Puzzles

Answers for this section
will be found on
pages 169–194

1. ALL THE KING'S HORSES

Here is a list of pictured articles. Each picture represents one syllable of a two-syllable word. You must decide what every picture represents and pair these drawings off to form commonly known words. For example, you might start with Number 7—a pad—and match it with Number 10—a lock—to form the word padlock.

2. WORD HUNTS

See how many words of four or more letters you can make out of each key word. Only one form of each word may be used, and no three-letter words can be counted as four by adding an 's' for the plural. The same letter may not be used twice unless it appears twice in the key word.

No. 1 LAUNCHED

There are at least 43 words to be taken out of LAUNCHED. Can you find 30 of them in 20 minutes?

1	*hand*	16	*dance*
2	*hend*	17	*dance*
3	*laden*	18	*deal*
4	*ache*	19	*lunch*
5	*head*	20	*clad*
6	*hunch*	21	*clued*
7	*staid*	22	*led*
8	*hand*	23	*lade*
9	*hand*	24	*uncle*
10	*heal*	25	*lead*
11	*heas*	26	*lends*
12	*Had*	27	*lance*
13	*Hale*	28	*chance*
14	*nude*	29	*hen*
15	*lace*	30	*hence*

No. 2 DYNAMITE

DYNAMITE contains at least 52 words. Can you find 40 of them in 25 minutes?

1	dye	21	meat
2	din	22	nit
3	dam	23	item
4	date	24	may
5	dim	25	mane
6	dime	26	mad
7	diet	27	amid
8	date	28	time
9	dame	29	team
10	die	30	tide
11	dome	31	tan
12	name	32	meat
13	mite	33	amid
14	mit	34	
15	mine	35	
16	mad	36	
17	made	37	
18	mane	38	
19	man	39	
20	mat	40	

No. 3 CHORISTER

There are at least 75 words in CHORISTER. Can you find 60 of them in 25 minutes?

1	21	41
2	22	42
3	23	43
4	24	44
5	25	45
6	26	46
7	27	47
8	28	48
9	29	49
10	30	50
11	31	51
12	32	52
13	33	53
14	34	54
15	35	55
16	36	56
17	37	57
18	38	58
19	39	59
20	40	60

3. P. Q. LAR CROSSWORD

ACROSS

1 Pigtails
5 Employ
6 Scrutinizes
7 Vegetable (plural)

DOWN

1 Gibe
2 Sarcastic remark
3 Witty sally
4 An odd, fantastic action

4. WORD MAZES

A word maze is worked by starting in any square you choose and moving from one adjoining square to the next in any direction—horizontally, vertically, or diagonally—until a complete word is formed. The words may be of two or more letters, but you must not enter the same square twice while you are spelling one word. With the exception of Word Maze #1, which is general, the mazes are made according to categories and the words you find must fit the category designated. After each word is completed, you may then choose any square, not necessarily an adjoining one, to start a new word.

No. 1 GENERAL

There are at least 188 common words to be found in this word maze. Can you find 150 in 30 minutes?

C	A	D	I	S
P	R	E	N	A
E	T	H	L	P
T	E	C	O	W
R	Y	N	R	E

No. 2 FOOD AND DRINK

There are at least 27 words to be found in this maze. Can you find 22 words in 25 minutes?

C	R	Y	T	W
I	E	E	A	N
B	A	L	M	O
N	T	S	S	B

1	15
2	16
3	17
4	18
5	19
6	20
7	21
8	22
9	23
10	24
11	25
12	26
13	27
14	

No. 3 FAMOUS PEOPLE, LIVING AND DEAD

There are at least 58 names to be found in this maze. Can you find 45 of them in 25 minutes?

L	E	S	T	A
A	W	I	L	D
R	D	N	E	L
P	O	G	A	B
E	O	H	R	O

1	16	31	46
2	17	32	47
3	18	33	48
4	19	34	49
5	20	35	50
6	21	36	51
7	22	37	52
8	23	38	53
9	24	39	54
10	25	40	55
11	26	41	56
12	27	42	57
13	28	43	58
14	29	44	
15	30	45	

No. 4 READY-TO-WEAR CLOTHES

There are at least 21 items of wearing apparel to be found in this maze. Can you find 18 in 25 minutes?

E	O	N	G
H	I	R	E
K	S	T	P
C	O	A	S
F	R	H	C

1 cap   12

2 skirt   13

3 ring   14

4 hook   15

5 hat   16

6 shirt   17

7   18

8   19

9   20

10   21

11

5. PERFECT SQUARES

Here are four five-by-five squares with two key words inserted in their proper places. You must find eight additional words to fill the entire square. The letters you fill in must spell a word, both vertically and horizontally.

Example below is a perfect square with one word repeated.

T	R	A	C	E
R	I	M	E	D
A	L	O	N	G
D	E	N	S	E
E	D	G	E	D

No. 1

One word is repeated in this puzzle.

C	H	A	N	T
R	o	v	e	r
E	v			a
S	e			c
T	r	a	c	e

No. 2

One word is repeated in this puzzle.

S	P	O	R	T
M				
A				
R				
T				

No. 3

No word is repeated in this puzzle.

				H
				U
				N
				T
H	E	R	E'	S

No. 4

No word is repeated in this puzzle.

S	T	A	F	F
C				
R				
I				
M				

6. HOOK-UP

The hook-up is a linking of two words that are commonly used together, such as the word "market" and the word "place." There are definitions for each word. Only one word goes in each square, but it must tie in with the word in the next square. For example: "market" and "place" go into squares No. 1 and No. 2, respectively. The word that goes into the No. 3 square must be commonly associated with the word "place" in square No. 2. And so on to the end of the puzzle. Here is a diagram, marked to show how the game is played.

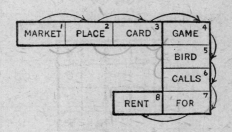

Definitions

1. Place to shop. (Answer: Market.) Fill the word market into the first square.
2. Arrange, set. (Answer: Place.) Fill into the diagram in Square 2.

You will note that market place is often hooked-up in everyday speech, as are place card, card game, game bird, etc.

Hook-up makes an excellent parlor game. One person may start a hooked-up word and then others follow around the room. Each person uses the last word offered to start his hook-up.

No. 1

1	2	3	4	5
				6
				7
12	11	10	9	8
13				
14				
15	16	17	18	19
				20
				21
26	25	24	23	22

Definitions

1 Roar, clap (in sky).
2 Rant and rave.
3 You can slam it, shut it, or leave it open.
4 Important in every woman's life.
5 If you have one, use a needle.
6 What a baseball player doesn't want to be.
7 Sometimes this is filled with corn.
8 Galahad's ___ was the Holy Grail.
9 Meats and mothers should be this.
10 Corns grow here too.
11 Your belt never is this after a big meal.
12 Crazy people do it when they are alone.
13 Colors should be this, and so should the horse you pick to win.
14 Some men are a slave to this—women usually complain there's too much of it.
15 You can lead this to water.
16 You are a member of the human one.
17 An unruly mob causes one and so do a lot of colors.
18 Should be confined to the theatre.
19 What goes ___ comes down.
20 All seats face it.
21 The opposite of this is plainly marked in all theatres.
22 Some people crash this.
23 With a few trimmings this becomes a home.
24 Something no man can be or no baby can be without.
25 This usually goes with kisses.
26 Some say it begins at forty.

No. 2

1	2	3	4	5
				6
				7
12	11	10	9	8
13				
14				
15	16	17	18	19
				20
				21
26	25	24	23	22

Definitions

1 Stalin's favorite color.
2 Sizzling.
3 This sets once a day.
4 Use this to get your number.
5 It has a ring that doesn't have to be insured.
6 Doctors are on this 24 hours a day.
7 "Keep your shirt ___."
8 Special kind of shoes.
9 It's an art, but even you can do it.
10 Walk all over it.
11 Made for dirty floors.
12 You can't fall this way.
13 An ant builds this.
14 A young William.
15 Gives milk.
16 What you love to touch.
17 Wells and great thinkers are this.
18 Made of water.
19 Neither front nor back.
20 Good to sit on.
21 A good one will bring a whistle.
22 No gallery is complete without it.
23 It's cut out for you.
24 There is one for multiplication.
25 Gangsters get under this.
26 Made of sugar and spice.

No. 3

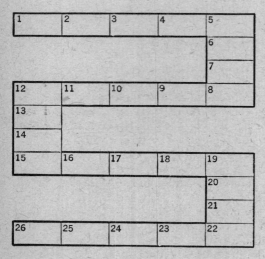

Definitions

1 Jack was advised to be this.
2 This jingles nicely in your pockets.
3 A hook-up.
4 You can wear it or hear it.
5 Every home has one.
6 Baldpate had seven. This square calls for o̶—̶
7 Sometimes you can't get one in.
8 You play it.
9 You need it to turn around.
10 Tear.
11 Not many things are this.
12 You always enjoy a square one.
13 Cops can give you one.
14 It's better to do this with your gloves on.
15 Comes in the middle of the day.
16 There are 8,760 of these in a year and leap year
   brings it to 8,784. This square calls for one.
17 You can look into it or through it.
18 It's an open and closed case.
19 You can have one with wisdom.
20 It's good for washing and spanking.
21 If lights are not on they are ___.
22 Every dog has its own.
23 Every word must have at least one.
24 Without fault.
25 It doesn't hurt when you strike one.
26 Pins do this to you.

7. SCRAMBLES

No. 1 RED-LETTER DAZE

Here is a list of scrambled red-letter days, each one placed opposite its symbol.

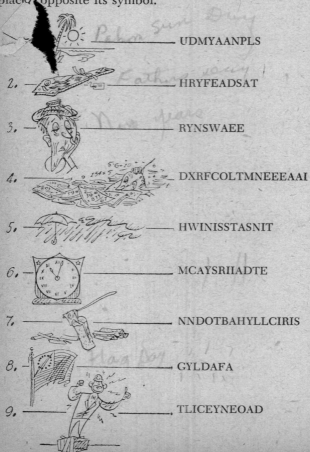

1. _____ UDMYAANPLS

2. _____ HRYFEADSAT

3. _____ RYNSWAEE

4. _____ DXRFCOLTMNEEEAAI

5. _____ HWINISSTASNIT

6. _____ MCAYSRIIADTE

7. _____ NNDOTBAHYLLCIRIS

8. _____ GYLDAFA

9. _____ TLICEYNEOAD

10. RBYADOLA

11. THMAICSRS

12. HGHTADIYBWRONNSSAIT

13. CDPIANDDEYENENE

14. GHTVKGIINNSA

15. NLANSIEVTISTANE

16. BCLAUYSMOUD

17. HRODAMTESY

18. SRAEET

19. ELHEWANOL

20. LDROMYAMAIE

No. 2 BOOKS AND AUTHORS

Opposite the scrambled author's name is the scrambled title of one of his famous books. Can you find out who and what each is?

Authors	*Titles*
1 CLSARTROWTESTI	HAVIONE
2 MEDPIDARUHARUNE	CRABEEC
3 VARLHEMEMELLIN	BICOKMYD
4 RETWANKILONESH	BRAFORREEMVE
5 WLANILIRESSIC	TTAIBBB
6 ENELODAFIED	NUROCIBORONESS
7 ANAWKIMRT	WETAMORSY
8 LATIMOCYALAUSOT	METOLLINEWT
9 NORELMTEBIY	TEHRGIWHUNESHGIT
10 MHRGSASMOUEMTAE	AMOGNDFHNBAEOU
11 HORUGECEFAFRECY	BANRUTALCYESERT

12 SHKLICDRNAESCE   APLDDCEVRIPEDIFO

_____   _____

13 OGULDDOSALLY   BRETOHE

_____   _____

14 KALASOJECCSHRN   WDESOKELENT

_____   _____

15 LMLTDMHTSAEHIEA   THAHEMNINT

_____   _____

No. 3 ANNIVERSARIES

There are symbols to mark each year of wedded
bliss. Can you unscramble the words opposite the
years?

1st Year	ERAPP
2nd Year	OALCCI
3rd Year	ISLUNM
4th Year	IKLS
5th Year	ODWO
6th Year	ROIN
7th Year	EPRPCO
8th Year	ZBOREN
9th Year	TROPYET
10th Year	INT
15th Year	SLTRACY
20th Year	HANIC
25th Year	RVEILS
30th Year	APLRE
35th Year	CROAL
40th Year	RYUB
45th Year	PHRISPAE
50th Year	LGOD
55th Year	DRELAME
75th Year	MADDION

8. FAMOUS QUOTATIONS

Famous quotations are used in the following puzzles. The quotations have been set up in crossword forms, but instead of definitions, one or two letters from each word have been filled into the diagrams in their proper places. The remaining letters of the quotations have been scrambled and put under the diagrams. Here is an example:

This is a quotation from Thomas Middleton's play "A Fair Quarrel," Act 5, Scene 1.

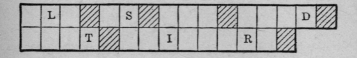

Scrambled Letters

A A E G G H I L L L N O O S T T T T

The diagram shows that the first word is a three-letter word with *L* as the second letter. Looking at the scrambled letters we see that the first word could be *ALL* or *ALE*. *All* is more likely to start a quotation so fill *A* and *L* into the diagram and cross *A* and *L* out of the list of scrambled letters. Now, the second word is a two-letter word ending in *S*. The word could be *IS* or *AS*. "All is" makes sense. So fill in *I*. . . . And so on until you have solved the puzzle. The answer to the sample puzzle is: "All is not gold that glitters."

No. 1

This expression was first used in an editorial by Horace Greeley in the New York *Herald Tribune* in 1859.

G			S		U			N		O	
W				

Scrambled Letters

A E E G G M N O O S T T W Y

No. 2

This expression was an order given by William Prescott to his American troops at the Battle of Bunker Hill on June 17, 1775.

	N			R			T		
O		C			E		T		
H			O				I		
	S	

Scrambled Letters

A D E E E E E E E F F H H I I I
L N N O R S S T T T U U W Y Y

No. 3

This is a quotation from Franklin D. Roosevelt's first Inaugural Address in Washington on March 4, 1933.

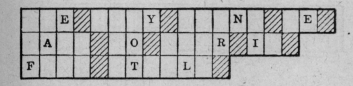

Scrambled Letters

A A E E E E F F G H H H I I
L N O R S S T T T V W

No. 4

This is a maxim used by Benjamin Franklin in *Poor Richard's Almanac.*

Scrambled Letters

A E E E E G H H H H L M M
O P P S S S T T T V

No. 5

This expression comes from John Heywood's *Book of Proverbs*, written in 1546.

Scrambled Letters

A B B D D D E E E H H I I
K M N O R S S U W W

No. 6

This famous quotation was written by Charles Kingsley in his book *A Farewell*.

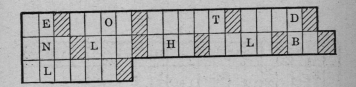

Scrambled Letters

A A B C D D E E E E E G I I
L M O O R S T V W W W

No. 7

This quotation was written by Alexander Pope in 1720 and printed in his *Epigram.*

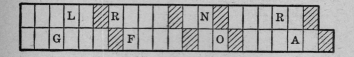

Scrambled Letters

A A D E E E E E F H H I L N
O O R R S S S T T U W

No. 8

This was written by Alfred Tennyson in *In Memoriam.*

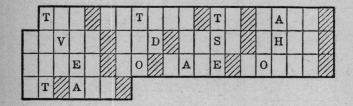

Scrambled Letters

A A A B D D E E E E E E H H I L L L L L
N N N O O O R R S T T T T V V V V

9.   ANAGRAMS

This game is similar to block anagrams, except that we have supplied the letter or letters to be added in order to make entirely new words. Example: *Tore* plus *U*. Answer: *Route*.

No. 1 ADD ONE LETTER

1 Pass	Plus	M	6 Ranting	Plus	O
2 Hopper	Plus	T	7 Chats	Plus	Y
3 Story	Plus	E	8 Diary	Plus	M
4 Rapt	Plus	A	9 Natty	Plus	R
5 Thigh	Plus	E	10 Acorn	Plus	H

No. 2 ADD TWO LETTERS

1 Rating	Plus E and M		6 Hint	Plus K and G	
2 Insane	Plus C and U		7 Sort	Plus B and U	
3 Miles	Plus U and B		8 Tripe	Plus C and H	
4 Crime	Plus A and G		9 Carts	Plus L and Y	
5 Leap	Plus P and A		10 Yet	Plus M and P	

No. 3 ADD THREE LETTERS

1 Queers	Plus L	U	B	6 Train	Plus O	M	C
2 Nuclei	Plus F	N	E	7 Rule	Plus T	E	C
3 Toil	Plus N	U	E	8 Paid	Plus L	O	M
4 Sharp	Plus D	O	Y	9 Chat	Plus A	R	R
5 Ripe	Plus A	R	I	10 The	Plus T	G	O

10. ADD A LETTER

Following are stories with missing words. The blanks indicate how many letters there are in each missing word. Every story starts with a one-letter word. By adding one letter, you make the next missing word. The letters may be transposed, but every missing word must contain all of the letters of the preceding missing word with one letter added. The words you form must fit into the text of the story.

Example: ". find . . impossible," said the man with the green . . . , "to perform this . . . . before you . . . . . the body."

The missing words are: I, it, tie, rite, inter.

No. 1

I was sitting reading . book . . the kitchen table when I saw a large . . . emerging from a hole in the wall. At any . . . . . I thought I saw him, but he was so quick there was no . . . . . of him for many minutes. I sat completely in a . . . . . . until I was . . . . I saw a motion in the open . . . . above the sink. Then my . . . . became normal and I got up on the nearest chair.

No. 2

. have never been taken . .
By cigars, cigarettes or . . .
When the drunks begin to . . . .
And smoker's tongues begin to . . . . .
As . . . . . . of remorse set in

I just . . . . . . with pride and grin

. . . . away from crowds of three,

. . . . don't appeal to me.

No. 3

a. man sat *at* a counter and . . . his lunch . . . . as
he was he still tarried to hear . . . . . of the Swiss
Alps which he was just about to climb. He rushed
home to pick up his boots, ... and pack. He
started off to reach the . . . . . . at the top of the
first rise before night. His guide had made the ascent
the day before with his . . . . And as he
climbed he had nothing to do but gaze at the
. . . . splendor of the golden sunset which
the . . . . of old could never simulate.

11. GOT YOUR NUMBER

No. 1

Twenty-four is placed correctly in the middle square
of the diagram below. Using the numbers on the ruler
shown, you should be able to make each line in every
direction (vertical, horizontal and diagonal) add up
to 72.

No. 2

Take numbers 1 through 25. By placing them in the proper positions make the diagram below total 65 in every direction (vertical, horizontal and diagonal). Do not repeat any number.

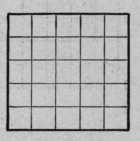

No. 3

Using the numbers 1 through 9, you should be able to make each line in every direction (vertical, horizontal and diagonal) add up to 15. Do not repeat any number.

No. 4

Using 3 through 27, you should make the lines in every direction (vertical, horizontal, diagonal) add up to 75. Do not repeat any number.

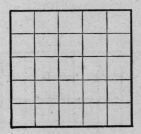

12.   THE MISSING VOWEL

Except for the missing vowels, the following story is complete. You must separate the words and insert a vowel where it is needed to make a word. We'll give you a hint. The same vowel is missing throughout the puzzle.

CRZYBRD, HPPYSLRK, STTBNDS
TNDNDSNGBLLD. WTCHMNSWM
DCHP, NGRYTGRMMRNDGHSTTCT,
GRBBLCKJCKNDSTRTFRCS. CRF
TYWTCHMN'SLRMHLTSPRTYND
MDCPSCLMLYSTLKWY.

13. WORD PUZZLES

No. 1

Make complete words using the listed letters un-
changed. They fit into the middle of the words. For
example: RYB. By adding C in front and ABY at the
end you form the word CRYBABY.

1	_____	RCHW	_____
2	_____	SPHY	_____
3	_____	MBSH	_____
4	_____	CHYD	_____
5	_____	PHTH	_____
6	_____	NSKR	_____
7	_____	CKSH	_____
8	_____	MYA	_____
9	_____	CS	_____
10	_____	SST	_____
11	_____	RW	_____
12	_____	AEST	_____
13	_____	LYC	_____
14	_____	RRH	_____
15	_____	LCY	_____
16	_____	MSTR	_____
17	_____	DK	_____
18	_____	SYL	_____
19	_____	HYTH	_____
20	_____	MV	_____

No. 2

The following letters, now in their proper sequence, are word endings. Add letter or letters in front to make a word.

1 _____ YLL

2 _____ RRH

3 _____ TU

4 _____ YSS

5 _____ FTH

6 _____ NCT

7 _____ AZZ

8 _____ TYR

9 _____ SC

10 _____ PTCY

No. 3

Can you find the words which contain the following double letters in sequence?

1 _____ AA _____

2 _____ II _____

3 _____ KK _____

4 _____ UU _____

5 _____ VV _____

No. 4

Name four words in the English language with four consecutive vowels.

1 _____

2 _____

3 _____

4 _____

No. 5

What are the common characteristics of these six words?

1 deft

2 sighing

3 calmness

4 canopy

5 first

6 stun

No. 6

Give two common words in which the vowels follow each other in alphabetical order (a e i o u).

1 _____

2 _____

No. 7

Rearrange these words to produce entirely different words.

1 relating   _____

2 dialect   _____

3 Madison   _____

4 coasting   _____

5 please   _____

6 models   _____

No. 8

1 Transpose funeral to make two words. _____

_____

2 Transpose Presbyterian to make three words. _____

_____

3 Transpose sweetheart to make three words. _____ _

_____

4 Transpose Spanish marriages to make four words. ___

_____

No. 9

Give a word beginning and ending in und. _____ _

_____

No. 10

The same six letters, differently arranged, will spell out the missing words in the following poem:

A _____ sat in his _____ gray
Watching the _____ of moonbeams play,
And as he sat, this was his lay:
"Thou _____ the weak; thou _____ the strong.
To thee the _____ of battles belong."
And the _____ of leaves echoed his song.

No. 11

Can you read and make sense out of the following dialogue?

"F U N E X?"
"S V F X."
"F U N E M?"
"S V F M."
"O K M N X."

14. A GARBLED SPEECH

The sentence below, which looks like Greek, is really a quotation from a famous speech. All of the letters of the speech are there. Not one has been added. It is up to you to figure out how to read it. It is so simple you can do it without a pencil.

No. Ww ear EEN. Gag edinag Rea. TCIV ilw artesti NGWH Ethe RTH atnat I on ora N.Y. NAti ons OCONCE I've dan. Dsod edi cat EDCA nl. on gendu RE.

15. CACHED FOOD

There are 21 different fruits and vegetables hidden in the following telegram. How many of them can you find? They may be located in one word or connecting words. They are in their proper sequence. Disregard punctuation marks.

WESTERN UNION

S.E. 308 D.L. PD-TDS. SANTA MONICA CALIF. 16
TO: MRS. O.K. RAVEN
    1061 FIFTH AVE.
    NEW YORK, N.Y.   DATE: MARCH 17, 1946
HAVE RUN INTO LIVE WIRE REAL-ESTATE AGENT AND BOUGHT HOUSE ON BEACH. BECAUSE OF HEAVY SCHEDULE I CAN'T RETURN. I PRESUME YOU WILL BE AN ANGEL AND CLOSE THE NEW YORK HOUSE ALONE. FIND LIVING HERE VERY CHEAP. PLEASE CALL PLUMBER AND HAVE HIM TURN OFF WATER AND LOOK INTO RANGE IN KITCHEN. ALSO HAVE PHONE COMPANY DISCONTINUE OUR NUMBER. RYE AND SCOTCH PLENTIFUL. IT'S A SUBLIME SPOT. A TORN PAIR OF PANTS FOR ME. FOR YOU A BATHING SUIT AND CAPE. ACHIEVES THE END I'VE ALWAYS LONGED FOR. AM IN FINE CONDITION. I ONLY HOPE YOU AND THE KIDS ARE THE SAME. WHEN I THINK OF THE PLAY AND MY OWN PART, I CHOKE WITH TEARS. BUT IN THE THEATRE MY HEAD BEGINS TO SPIN. ACHES AND PAINS CONSTANTLY RECUR. RANTING SHAKESPEARE AND TEMPESTUOUS BEETHOVEN ARE NOT FOR ME. I WILL SPEAK TO YOU ON SATURDAY AND WILL SEND YOU SNAPS OF THE NEW HOUSE AND THE MAGNIFICENT BEACH.

                          ARDENTLY YOURS
                          OLLY

16. MAP OF THE

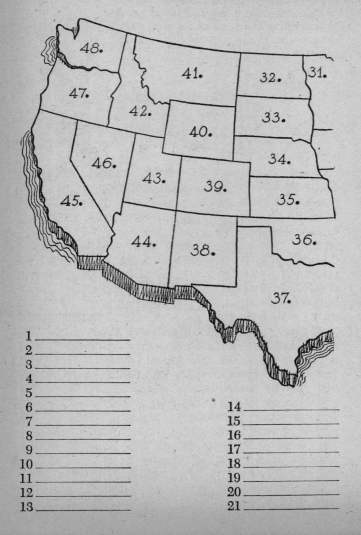

1 _____
2 _____
3 _____
4 _____
5 _____
6 _____
7 _____
8 _____
9 _____
10 _____
11 _____
12 _____
13 _____

14 _____
15 _____
16 _____
17 _____
18 _____
19 _____
20 _____
21 _____

UNITED STATES

Each state has been numbered on the map. Fill in the name of the state next to the corresponding number in the lines below.

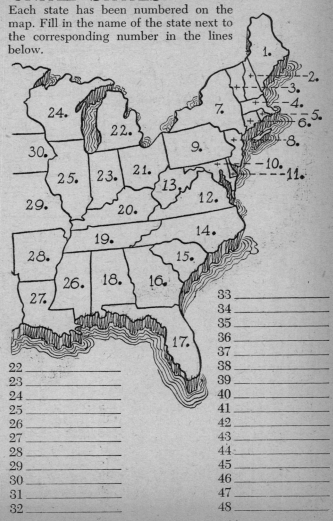

22 _____
23 _____
24 _____
25 _____
26 _____
27 _____
28 _____
29 _____
30 _____
31 _____
32 _____

33 _____
34 _____
35 _____
36 _____
37 _____
38 _____
39 _____
40 _____
41 _____
42 _____
43 _____
44 _____
45 _____
46 _____
47 _____
48 _____

17. SYNONYMS

Determine the word which is synonymous with all three definitions.

No. 1

All answers begin with B

1 carton, to spar, lodge _box_

2 dance, round toy, projectile _ball_

3 hit, baseball necessity, drunken spree _bat_

4 help, part of the body, reverse _back_

5 strip, group, orchestra _band_

6 to sag, catch, women's accessory _bag_

7 monthly statement, bird's beak, legal action _bill_

_____

8 drinking place, to keep out, a legal profession _bar_

_____

9 rivulet, faint sound, talk _babble_

10 a foundation, part of a diamond, low _base_

11 blighted hope, knock, puff _blow_

12 a subterfuge, shutter, unseeing _blind_

13 street, hinder, toy _block_

14 mislead, cliff, ungracious _bluff_

No. 2

All answers in this group begin with D.

1 rush, line, sprinkling ___dash___

2 distribute, barter, a piece of pine or fir wood ___
___deal___

3 envoy, consign, substitute ___delegate___

4 malady, turmoil, confusion ___disorder___

5 select, potion, sketch ___draft___

6 attract, describe, sketch ___draw___

7 treat, attire, berate ___dress___

8 musical instrument, part of ear, oil container ___
___Drum___

9 fruit, engagement, part of calendar ___date___

10 adorn, platform of planks, amount of cards ___
___Deck___

11 sink, reject, slope downward ___decline___

12 printer's errand boy, spirit of evil, to season an egg
___devil___

13 servant, tame animal, homemade ___domestic___

14 political border, paint, dog disease ___distemper___

18. LITERARY CRYPTS

A cryptogram is writing in cipher. Every letter is part of a code that remains constant throughout the puzzle. "B," for instance, may stand for "E," and "M" for "L." The experienced cryptographer seeks first to spot the vowels, and looks for letters that recur frequently to give him his clue.

"Literary Crypts" appear weekly in *The Saturday Review of Literature*. They are familiar quotations from the works of famous men.

No. 1

ABCD BEF AGHF IJKCFKD CLGIL IBMIL
DNBAA OAGFD, KPM AFM CBDQD BRS
LJERFMD KEFBH MLEJPTL. _____

                    UJRBMLBR DCGOM

No. 2

GB NBAK BCKHKNP RH GSK OKXRCCRCX
BP L NRPK-NBCX DBELCWK. _____

                    BHWLD TRNFK

No. 3

BSL DSCGKCPCP MQ BCFL OGCHPA CH CBA
ELHPLXHTL. _____

                    BSL OXGR

No. 4

R CFRLAFM TCDPSNFRM XG R HLFRKFL
TCDPSNFRM KNRA RA XHADLRAK DAF.____

TFAWRBXA QLRASCXA

No. 5

BMACRK LX ABR NDEMCKX CRFRGHR ODC
PRLGH LGALTLKMARK. _____

H. P. XBME

No. 6

FNPBNCH HKN HKBDFN RHCNGM LTCH
SN HKN MDDHCHDDG DM KTLRGRHX.____

LDFHWDLNBX

No. 7

KBX HCG MCOAXFOZ KBX KSWT, OCK
BRFZXPH. _____

D. QPWLX

No. 8

ZY XWU VUTZSRY RQ PROXW—XWUNU ZM

YR MOSW LRNK JM QJZV. _____

IOVLUN-VPXXRY

No. 9

CLNCK N ANTBNOC STYN CLNC PNFY YNC

LBK RFYNDSNKC GO CLY TBH GS N TBGO.

_____

E. KLNDYKHYNFY

No. 10

DGARBDP CG DHHKC FHSGFEBDP XC GA-

RHF LHGLMHC RXTBAC. _____

EXFZ ANXBD

19. CRAZY CRYPTS

No. 1

NOFVMPFD NOBDL, FH NORKP
ME NOBFHP NOBSPW, NORSFRK
NORSOJMOK NOBRKPMS SR NOB-
JFPT ME NOBSPW NORRH.

No. 2

DFMAABH KC MEGLCBKH OK-
AKKW PHRTPX RJMW PHBTP-
PHKTP XCKHZ KHZ BDDMZBKC-
MQG XKQKKDX CR KQQKV.

No. 3

FKA FCGPMGB FDLOMG. KEQNQ:
SBHTOQKLGQBL'B PQKWADBQB
DX DMPQSCB TDFSEMJ.

No. 4

KBGAC KBGHNTABNF OBPAMA
DPOPWLM AEMOCLM, CBLMM
ABMMCA CG CBM RTZS.

No. 5

M B K A G   M B G F C L H B K F D N B

P N M R F D N B Z   M A N M D L Z E L O K S R K T

C N E N H B K F D G   K T P   H N C Z F B R A N

K Z   N Q F N B C   E R T H W R Z C.

No. 6

F M B D C L P F C K   M R K   A F V K A   G B A M

R R F T E R F H   R A   N C C,   F P K O S A B D X

B D   O D B E P F K R S   W F R L R K.

20. CODES

No. 1

Perhaps you have always had a secret longing to be a spy. One of the brain-racking jobs in Military and Naval Intelligence is the cracking of enemies' codes. In the tests which follow, you will have a chance to discover whether or not you have any aptitude along these lines.

Here are three messages in code. Below each message there appears a translation. You must discover from the code and the translation the system which was used in coding the message. Then write the answer, using the same code which was used for the message.

1

Coded Message: LNUD RTOOKHDR SNMHFGS.

DECIPHERED: MOVE SUPPLIES TONIGHT.

ANSWER: Can't. Moon too bright. *Use the same code.*

use following letter

2

Coded Message: CF31K5 1753K K5E.

DECIPHERED: LOCATE AGENT TEN.

ANSWER: Checked. Believed dead. *Use the same code.* _____

3

Coded Message: WJUTWY SARGJW TK JSJRE XM-NUX NS UTWY.

DECIPHERED: REPORT NUMBER OF ENEMY SHIPS IN PORT.

ANSWER: Sixteen cruisers anchored. *Use the same code.* _____

No. 2

An American spy, noted for his love of puzzles, was stationed in Paris during the German occupation. He received the following puzzle through the mail. The German censors allowed it to be delivered after examining it closely. Unknown to them, it contained an important message for the American. Can you decipher it?

1	2	3	4	▨	5	6	▨
7	8	9	10	11	12	13	14
15	16	▨	17	18	19	20	21
▨	22	23	24	25	26	27	28

1 Cut flowers __ __ __ __ __ __ __

2 Make effort to hear *l i s t e n*

3 Leave out *o m i t*

4 Puff of air *d r a f t*

5 Employ *u s e*

6 Metrical composition *s o n g*

7 Grown up __ __ __ __ __

8 Man *m a l e*

9 Disable *l a r m*

10 Vase with foot *u r n*

11 Short sleep _N_ _a_ _P_

12 Frozen water _i_ _c_ _e_

13 Converse _t_ _a_ _l_ _k_

14 Sick _i_ _l_ _l_

15 Indistinct __ __ __ __ __ __ __

16 Nation's warships _N_ _a_ _v_ _y_

17 Feel aversion to __ __ __ __ __ __ __ __

18 Overturn __ __ __ __ __

19 Fully developed __ __ __ __ __ __

20 Gone by __ __ __ __

21 Of sound mind __ __ __ __

22 Meddle __ __ __ __ __ __

23 Uneven __ __ __

24 God of sea __ __ __ __ __ __ __

25 Contrary to law __ __ __ __ __ __ __

26 Horrible __ __ __ __ __

27 Bed of netting __ __ __ __ __ __

28 Dark thick liquid _T_ _a_ _r_

No. 3 CODE LETTER

The following, innocent-looking letter, was intercepted by an alert detective. It contained a message which might have caused disastrous consequences, had it not been discovered. Can you find the key and decode the message?

July Fifth, 1944

Dear Will,

Can you take me to Bert's with you on Sat. Webster's car is broken and won't run. The man at Herman's repair shop stayed and worked again. He was at work for two days. Result nil. I won't see you now until Fri. Hope Ed's better.

Chuck

No. 4 CODE DIRECTORY

This is a facsimile of one of the pages of an address book sent by a member of Military Intelligence, presumably for safekeeping, to a staff officer at Headquarters. It passed all enemy censors, despite the fact that it contained a vital message. Can you, given only the key page, decipher it?

NAME		ADDRESS
DAGIN,	Campbell	420 Park Ave.
DAINSWORTH,	Printers	300 Lafayette St.
DALTON,	Walter	30 Bolton Blvd.
DAMENN,	Everett	7 Sutton Place South
DEARBORN,	Fishmarket	350 Third Ave.
DETCHMAN,	Winthrop	352 Park Place
DEWEY,	George	675 Pace St.
DIAPER,	Service	36 Elm St.
DIFTON,	Peter	230 Riverside Drive
DIPPSMITH,	Ethel	16 West 11th St.
DOCALL,	Theresa	16 West 11th St.
DOLTMAN,	Frank	32 Beverly Drive
DORRANCE,	Insurance Co.	30 Broad Street
DOVOE,	Katherine	25 Fifth Ave.
DOWLEY,	Florist	751 Fifth Ave.
DRATTLE,	Alfred	21 Broadway
DREW,	Market	375 Third Ave.
DRUEMAN,	Floyd	356 Madison Ave.
DUNN,	Laundry	2453 Second Ave.
DUNTON,	Fred	24 West 12th St.
DURYEA,	Ernest	35 Biltmore Terrace

21. WORD PYRAMIDS

No. 1

All the words which appear in a word pyramid begin
and end in the same letter. Thus, if you find the correct
answer to any one of the words, you have the clue to
the rest. Each word has a definition, and each of the
pyramids has a different key letter.

1 __ __ __

2 __ __ __ __

3 __ __ __ __ __

4 __ __ __ __ __ __

5 __ __ __ __ __ __ __

6 __ __ __ __ __ __ __ __

7 __ __ __ __ __ __ __ __ __

8 __ __ __ __ __ __ __ __ __ __

Definitions

1 Contrive to make a living.
2 Rim.
3 Bird of prey.
4 Fit to be eaten.
5 To lament for the dead.
6 Demonstrative, gushing.
7 Powerful, striking.
8 Womanish.

No. 2

```
    1 __ __ __
   2 __ __ __ __
  3 __ __ __ __ __
 4 __ __ __ __ __ __
5 __ __ __ __ __ __
6 __ __ __ __ __ __ __ __
7 __ __ __ __ __ __ __ __ __
8 __ __ __ __ __ __ __ __ __
9 __ __ __ __ __ __ __ __
10 __ __ __ __ __ __ __ __
11 __ __ __ __ __ __ __
12 __ __ __ __ __ __
13 __ __ __ __ __
14 __ __ __ __
15 __ __ __
```

Definitions

1 Play by Karel Capek.   2 River in Germany.
3 Stream of water.   4 Spitefulness.
5 Real-estate salesman.   6 Arctic antlered animal.
7 Town in New York State.   8 Think over.
9 Adjuster.   10 Book in which entries are made.
11 Climbing rose.   12 Forest warden.
13 Instrument used for shaving.   14 To bring up.
15 Reading, writing and arithmetic.

No. 3

1 _ _ _
2 _ _ _ _
3 _ _ _ _ _
4 _ _ _ _ _ _
5 _ _ _ _ _ _ _
6 _ _ _ _ _ _ _ _
7 _ _ _ _ _ _ _ _ _
8 _ _ _ _ _ _ _ _ _ _

Definitions

1 Parent.
2 Ceased to live.
3 Shrink from.
4 Ward off.
5 Go down.
6 A share in profits.
7 Breed of dog.
8 Dissolute.

22. CHANGING WORDS

You must change one word into another in this puzzle. By substituting one letter at a time, a new word is made with each change. For example: Change *Lady* into *Male* in three moves. *Lady, Lade, Made, Male.*

1 Change TAKE to SEND in four moves.
2 Change DRY to WET in five moves.
3 Change FOUR to FIVE in seven moves.
4 Change HARD to SOFT in five moves.

5 Change FISH to FOWL in seven moves.

6 Change LOSE to FIND in four moves.

7 Change HEAD to FOOT in five moves.

8 Change WIDE to LONG in five moves.

9 Change PAL to FOE in four moves.

10 Change WORK to PLAY in eight moves.

23. FUN WITH WORDS

No. 1

Use the letters in the word REST to make completely new words. The letters will have to be rearranged and fitted into the blank spaces below. The letters we have put in are in their proper places and may not be changed. Each letter of the word REST must be used in every word.

1 _ _ S I _ _

2 A _ R _ _ _

3 I N _ _ _ _

4 B _ I _ _ L _

5 C H A _ _ R _ U _ E

6 P A _ _ U _ _

7 D E S C R IP T ION
8 I N T ERP R I S E
9 FLU S T e r
10 S T R IK E
11 R E S OR T
12 S CA T T E R
13 R E S P _ C T
14 S HOR T E N
15 S T O R e

No. 2

Use the letters in the word CART to make completely new words.

1 T r a c K
2 T a c t i _
3 T r a c E
4 r a c KE t
5 c a s t o r
6 c r a E t
7 T r a N c E
8 c a t o r
9 c a r PE t
10 C H A r t
11 c a R R o t
12 r E a c t
13 c a r t EL
14 c a r t ON
15 c L a r E t

24. CONCENTRATION TESTS

The following test will mean nothing unless completed under pressure of time. See how you can do within *10* minutes.

No. 1

How many times do the initials of George Washington and Abraham Lincoln appear together in their proper sequence in the jumbled letters below? They must appear ALGW or GWAL to be counted.

ALWGZDALGWstvawglALGVALGWGWALLAGW
ZVRTYGWALGWZTOMNWGLALGWZTNLAWGW
LATUVBMKWALSGWALLWGLWGALSTUgwallw
wwwGWTUVWALVVNOPQGWALAGWLAPTVYR
STGWALWGLALWGWALGwLaLgwGWALSBMP
QWRGLAWGWALaWGSGWalsvmGWAL

No. 2

What is the total number of times the numeral 4 appears before 5 when the 5 is followed by a 2, and the number of times 3 is followed by 6 when the 6 is followed by 1?

45463614524563145263113452360631452453613603 6154
24513614526312452365436134536043614523612454 5263
16489361165445453698459872136163154245225487 6368
45036145287450368452364536145094526783645236 3610
94

No. 3

Count the number of times you can spell the word *rest* out of the list of letters below. Do not use a letter twice.

ertuvwxslvwrtuviesabdjklruvwtemnsrevjmtmnopqwlm
srvraspqmneoztlfgrdsophgfeaswqtrlrvremogqodtlmnor
rjkelmegtuvwxyzabcreslmnoptqgdfrabghodelbcjqrtmn
qeygsfbnopabcfghijkopqrstovwxygqressssttllmmoodd

No. 4

The following test is based on a mathematical principle for each row of numbers. Try to decipher it and fill in the missing numbers in the blank spaces.

(1) 3 6 12 . . . . .   48 96 . . . 384 . . . 1536
(2) 2 3 5 . . . 12 17 . . . 30 38 . . . 57 . . .
(3) 5 . . . 6 3 7 4 . . . 5 9 . . . 10 7 11
    8 . . . . . 13 10
(4) 2 4 . . . 48 . . . 1440 . . . 80,640 . . . . .
(5) 24192 12096 . . . 3024 . . . 756 . . . 189.

No. 5

Add the following numbers in your head.

1 One thousand and thirty and one thousand and thirty and thirty and ten. _____

2 A man came to a hill that was one mile up and one mile down. He went up the hill at fifteen miles an hour. How fast would he have to come down to make his average for the entire hill thirty miles an hour, up and down? _____

3a How many one-cent postage stamps are there in a dozen? _____

 b How many two-cent postage stamps are there in a dozen? _____

25. BRAIN PUZZLERS

No. 1 CHAIN PUZZLE

A farmer came to a blacksmith with five pieces of chains, of three links each, as illustrated.

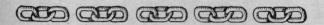

The farmer wanted them all made into one continuous chain. The blacksmith said, "I charge one cent to cut a link and one cent to weld a link, so the charge will be eight cents."

"No," said the farmer, "I figure the charge will be only six cents."

The farmer was right. How did he figure this out?

No. 2

Can you make the diagram shown below with one continuous line? You may not lift your pencil from the paper.

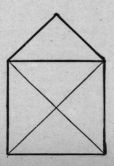

26. FAMOUS "CARS"

All of the following definitions describe words that begin with the letters CAR. An example definition: "What 'CAR' is handy with a hammer?" would be answered with the word CARpenter. How many can you find?

1 What CAR is becoming, warm and easy to wear?

2 What CAR is your coffee poured from?

3 What CAR is sweet on the tooth?

4 What CAR was used to open up the unknown West?

5 What CAR do secretaries use daily?

6 What CAR is unpleasant on the neck, nose, etc.?

7 What CAR do hunters bring home?

8 What CAR don't you want when you sit for a portrait?

9 What CAR doesn't always mix with marriage?

10 What CAR do babies love to get?

11 What CAR comes to town and makes merry?

12 What CAR do rabbits love?

13 What CAR do sculptors excel in?

14 What CAR made Hitler unhappy to look at in 1945?

15 What CAR do you order your diamonds by?

27. DOODLES

Everyone, at some time or other, doodles. We've made some lines below. Use your imagination and transform the lines into recognizable pictures. Famous people have drawn pictures from these same crude beginnings. Compare yours with theirs.

No. 1

No. 2

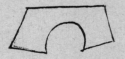

No. 3

No. 4

No. 5

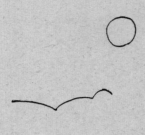

No. 6

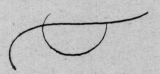

No. 7

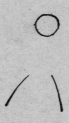

No. 8

28. DETECT THE M'S

Study this picture carefully and see how many **objects** you can name that begin with the letter M. We shall start you off by showing you the *MAN* who is a *MAJOR*. There are 40 others. How many can you find?

29. MEMORY TEST

Study this picture carefully for three minutes and try to imprint each object indelibly in your mind. Then close the book and see how many of the twenty objects you can remember.

30. BRIDGE PROBLEMS

No. 1
NORTH
♠ A 3 2
♥ A J 9 8
♦ K J 9 2
♣ A 9

WEST
♠ Q 8 7
♥ 6 3
♦ 8 7 6
♣ 10 5 4 3 2

EAST
♠ K 10
♥ 10 5 4
♦ Q 10 5 4
♣ K J 8 7

SOUTH
♠ J 9 6 5 4
♥ K Q 7 2
♦ A 3
♣ Q 6

South must make 6 spades against perfect defense.
Opening lead—6 of Hearts by West.

No. 2
NORTH
♠ 5 3
♥ Q 10 8 2
♦ 10 9
♣ K Q 6 3 2

WEST
♠ Q 7 6 2
♥ J 6 4
♦ K Q J 8 7
♣ 4

EAST
♠ J 9 8
♥ K 9 7
♦ 6 5 4 2
♣ J 10 5

SOUTH
♠ A K 10 4
♥ A 5 3
♦ A 3
♣ A 9 8 7

South must make 3 No-Trump.
Opening lead—King of Diamonds by West.

No. 3
NORTH
♠ A 3 2
♥ K Q 3 2
♦ A 3 2
♣ A K 2

WEST
♠ 10 8
♥ J 9 8 7
♦ K 7 6 5
♣ 9 7 3

EAST
♠ K Q J 9
♥ 10 6 5
♦ 4
♣ Q J 10 5 4

SOUTH
♠ 7 6 5 4
♥ A 4
♦ Q J 10 9 8
♣ 8 6

South must make 5 Diamonds against perfect defense.

West leads 10 of Spades.

No. 4
NORTH
♠ A J 9
♥ A 5 4 3
♦ K Q J
♣ A 6 5

WEST
♠ 7 6 4
♥ K Q J 10 7 6
♦ 9 2
♣ Q J

EAST
♠ 5 3 2
♥ 9 8
♦ 8 7 6 5
♣ 10 9 8 3

SOUTH
♠ K Q 10 8
♥ 2
♦ A 10 4 3
♣ K 7 4 2

South must make 7 Spades against perfect defense. Opening lead—King of Hearts by West.

No. 5

NORTH
♠ A Q 6 5
♥ 10 5 3
♦ Q 4
♣ A J 10 8

WEST
♠ K J 8
♥ Q 7
♦ A 5 3
♣ K 9 5 4 2

EAST
♠ 10 7 3
♥ A 6 2
♦ J 10 9 8 7 6
♣ 7

SOUTH
♠ 9 4 2
♥ K J 9 8 4
♦ K 2
♣ Q 6 3

South must make 3 No-Trump against perfect defense.

Opening lead—4 of Clubs by West.

Quizzes

Answers for this section
will be found on
pages 194–208

1. OBSERVATION QUIZ

1 How many times does the numeral one (1) or the word one appear on a one-dollar bill—not counting the serial numbers?

2 What suits of regular playing cards have one-eyed Jacks?

3 Does the red or green light appear on top of a traffic signal?

4 Whose face appears on a five-dollar bill?

5 How many keys are there on a standard typewriter?

6 Do the buttonholes of a man's shirt run vertically or horizontally?

7 Is the hour hand above or below the minute hand on a watch?

8 Do men's coats button to the right or the left?

9 On which side is the bow on a man's hat?

10 Whose face appears on a ten-dollar bill?

11 Which stripe appears at the top of the American flag—the red or the white?

12 In a deck of playing cards, which king is in profile?

13 How are the pips of an eight arranged on playing cards?

14 On which side of the sink is the hot water tap usually found?

15 Is the money-return slot of a public telephone on your right or left side?

16 In which hand does the Statue of Liberty hold her torch?

17 Does the eagle's head face right or left on a quarter?

18 Whose name appears last on the list of credits at the beginning of every movie?

19 Does a full piano keyboard begin with one or two white keys?

20 How many toes has a chicken?

2. AUTHOR QUIZ

The answers to the following definitions consist of the names of famous authors. Some are given as a whole; some are divided into two syllables. Example: *To yearn* and *a comrade*. Answer: *To yearn* would be "long" and *comrade*, defined, would be "fellow." Result: *Longfellow*.

1 A drama and part of the foot.
2 Meat and short for a singer's paradise.
3 A job and a gentleman.
4 Everyone and a bed.
5 A guffaw and a prickly object.
6 What a drunk would call a gentleman; a forest.
7 A playground and a thoughtful hesitation.
8 You direct him to go home.
9 It shall never meet.
10 A vehicle and a type of stocking.
11 A greater amount and a meadow.
12 An inlet and to study with care.
13 Come in first and to fly.
14 What a Chinese does to peas.
15 What you shouldn't raise.
16 A chicken's home and a domestic animal's sound of pleasure.
17 A small rise and a weight.
18 A beer mug.
19 An exclamation of disgust.
20 One who walks without purpose.
21 A German river and what keeps you going.
22 He who calls, "Hubba-hubba."
23 To act and a familiar term for a parent.
24 Abbreviation for a tome and a rip.
25 A vowel and to soak up.

3. COMMON DENOMINATOR QUIZ

1 What have the following playwrights in common?

> Edna Ferber
> Moss Hart
> Marc Connelly

2 What have the following words in common?

> frigid
> skiing
> distinct

3 What have the following women in common?

> Joan of Arc
> Molly Pitcher
> Queen Boadicea

4 What have the following musical plays in common?

> *Oklahoma!*   *Carousel*   *Going Up*

5 What have the following Presidents in common?

> Ulysses S. Grant
> William McKinley
> Warren G. Harding

6 What have the following authors in common?

> George Sand
> Taylor Caldwell
> Isak Dinesen

7 What have the following men in common?

> Charles Curtis
> Thomas Marshall
> William A. Wheeler

8 What have the following comic-strip characters in common?

> Anne Howe   Daisy Mae   Olive Oyl

9 What have the following best-selling novels in common?

> *Gone With the Wind   Forever Amber
> The Black Rose*

10 What have the following Presidents in common?

> John Tyler   Andrew Johnson
> Calvin Coolidge

11 What have the following men in common?

> Abner Doubleday
> Marquess of Queensberry

12 What have these two musicians in common?

> Beethoven   Smetana

13 What have these men in common?

> Anton J. Cermak
> James A. Garfield
> King Alexander of Serbia

14 What have the following in common?

> Phileas Fogg
> Sir Francis Drake
> Wendell Willkie

15 What have the following men in common?

> Baron Rothschild
> Disraeli
> Alexander Hamilton

4. KNOW YOUR ADS?

What products have the following advertising slogans made famous?

1 Good to the last drop.
2 Ask the man who owns one.
3 Eventually, why not now?
4 Not a cough in a carload.
5 Reach for a _____ instead of a sweet.
6 The pause that refreshes.
7 The voice with the smile wins.
8 99-44/100 per cent pure.
9 Four out of five have it.
10 No metal can touch you.
11 Men of Distinction.
12 The beer that made Milwaukee famous.
13 When it rains it pours.
14 Look sharp, feel sharp and be sharp.
15 The soap for beautiful women.
16 His Master's Voice.
17 Our hand has never lost its skill.
18 Time to retire.
19 Banishes tattle-tale gray.
20 Drink it and sleep.

5. HOW WELL DO YOU KNOW YOUR ANIMALS?

No. 1

1 Where did the jackrabbit get its name?
2 How should a live rabbit be lifted?
3 Do beavers eat fish?

4 Do all species of monkeys use their tails as a fifth hand?

5 How do elephants bend their legs in lying down?

6 Is there a backbone in a camel's hump?

7 What is a cow's cud?

8 Do dogs sweat?

9 Is a zebra a light animal with dark stripes or a dark animal with light stripes?

10 On what legs do sheep rise first after lying down?

No. 2

What are the following groups of animals called? For example: a FLOCK of sheep.

1 _____ of ants

2 _____ of bears

3 _____ of bees

4 _____ of cattle

5 _____ of elephants

6 _____ of fish

7 _____ of geese

8 _____ of grouse

9 _____ of hounds

10 _____ of lions

11 _____ of partridge

12 _____ of peacocks

13 _____ of pheasants

14 _____ of quail

15 _____ of roes

16 _____ of whales

17 _____ of wolves

What are the feminine forms for the following animals? For example: *Hen* is the feminine counterpart of *rooster*.

18 boar   _____

19 buck   _____

20 bull   _____

21 drake   _____

22 fox   _____

23 gander   _____

24 lion   _____

25 ram   _____

26 stallion   _____

27 stag   _____

28 tiger   _____

What are the young of the following animals called? For example: a *kitten* is a young *cat*.

29 bear   _____

30 bull   _____

31 cow   _____

32 chicken   _____

33 deer   _____

34 dog   _____

35 duck   _____

36 elephant   _____

37 frog   _____

38 goose   _____

39 hen   _____

40 horse   _____

41 lion	_____
42 sheep	_____
43 swan	_____
44 swine	_____
45 seal	_____
46 salmon	_____

6. MYTHICAL CITIES

Here is a list of mythical cities. Can you match each one with an abbreviation of one of the states of the Union? Each city calls for a different state which will complete either an expression or a word. For example: The mythical city Coca attached to the abbreviation of Colorado (Colo.) makes Coca-Colo. As example shows, puns are not only allowed, but suggested.

CITY	STATE	CITY	STATE
1 Deathly		13 Fiven	
2 Ala		14 Farmerina	
3 Uno		15 Shapeless	
4 Income		16 Either	
5 Praise		17 Vita	
6 Proan		18 Ga	
7 Oola		19 Maan	
8 Wet		20 Goodness	
9 Noaz		21 Squee	
10 Hitor		22 Can	
11 Perk		23 Expedie	
12 Musee			

7. IT'S ALL ENGLISH

Give the American equivalents for the following English words:

1 Wireless   _____

2 Lift   _____

3 Tram   _____

4 Ladder   _____

5 Bobby   _____

6 Pub   _____

7 Hoarding   _____

8 Petrol   _____

9 Fortnight   _____

10 Suspenders   _____

11 Goods train   _____

12 Lines   _____

13 Physical jerks   _____

14 Walk out   _____

15 Queue   _____

8. SPELLING TESTS

No. 1

Fill in the plurals of the following words.

1 church	_____	14 life	_____
2 elf	_____	15 mouse	_____
3 forgo	_____	16 motto	_____
4 echo	_____	17 key	_____
5 army	_____	18 self	_____
6 foot	_____	19 man	_____
7 gas	_____	20 maestro	_____
8 lady	_____	21 potato	_____
9 hobo	_____	22 portico	_____
10 knife	_____	23 cameo	_____
11 radio	_____	24 folio	_____
12 tango	_____	25 cargo	_____
13 mercy	_____		

No. 2

Below are words which are commonly misspelled. Test your friends' spelling by reading them aloud.

1 commission
2 conceit
3 bicycle
4 breathe
5 canceling
6 abbreviate
7 already
8 asylum
9 besiege
10 courageous
11 parallel
12 rhythm
13 sergeant
14 separator
15 succeed
16 wherever
17 yacht
18 infallible
19 intelligible
20 exaggerate
21 extraordinary
22 facsimile
23 prejudice
24 peculiar
25 loathe
26 impresario
27 inoculation
28 innuendo
29 necessary
30 occurrence
31 aggressor
32 adviser
33 harass
34 obsessed
35 possessed

9. TEST YOUR GRAMMAR

Select the proper word, given in parentheses, in order to complete the following sentences correctly.

"I am (coming, going) to your house for the poems (that, which) (are, were) written by Shelley," Mabel said. "I should like to (bring, take) the book home and (bring, take) it back to you tomorrow. I (will, shall) be careful of it. Everyone, boys and girls alike in our class, (is, are) required to read it. The highest grade will go to (whomever, whoever) turns in the best report. Everyone (can, may) read the book at home if (they, he) (choose, chooses)."

10. PICK THE CORRECT DEFINITION

1 EMOLUMENT — A medicinal balm, profit, celebration, soothing.

2 INDIGENOUS — Native, needy, dyspeptic, blurred.

3 CURSIVE — Censorial, superficial, profane, flowing.

4 HETEROGENEOUS — Orthodox, pertaining to a six sided figure, diverse, strong.

5 LIMN — A boundary, calcium deposit, draw, pedigree.

6 MACERATE — Tear, pray, soften by soaking, venerate.

7 AMELIORATE — Walk about, hide, improve, make tractable.

8 CASTIGATE — Behead, beat, fortify, cast off.

9 SOPHISTRY — Pride, obstinacy, harmony, fallacy.

10 MODICUM — Method, average, a little, modern.

11 NOXIOUS — Unwholesome, loud, novel, pompous.

12 PREPONDERATE — Outweigh, haughty, absurd, meditate before.

13 SUCCINCT — Sweet, vacuous, clear, terse.

14 INNUENDO — Simplicity, alias, insinuation, incongruous.

11. CHOICE TEST

Check the correct answer to each of the following questions.

1 A lodestone is a:
    a Magnetic iron ore.
    b A stone used for foundations.
    c A semiprecious jewel.

2 How many amendments are there of the Constitution?
    a 51   b 33   c 21

3 Which one of the following men was the Republican nominee for vice-president in 1940, when Wendell Willkie ran for president?
    a John Bricker
    b Frank R. Knox
    c Charles L. McNary

4 The Reverend C. L. Dodgson wrote under the pen name:
    a Francis H. Hardy
    b Lewis Carroll
    c Artemus Ward

5 The building which has been called "the cradle of American liberty" is better known as:
    a Independence Hall
    b Faneuil Hall
    c Old Statehouse

6 Lake Superior is the largest of the Great Lakes. Which lake is next largest?
    a Lake Michigan
    b Lake Huron
    c Lake Ontario

7 In what year was the first trans-Atlantic wireless message sent?
    a 1895   b 1902   c 1910

8 Whose name headed the list of signers of the Declaration of Independence?
  a Samuel Adams
  b John Hancock
  c Benjamin Franklin

9 Who wrote SPOON RIVER ANTHOLOGY?
  a Edgar Lee Masters
  b Carl Sandburg
  c Edna St. Vincent Millay

10 Who was the founder of Hull House in Chicago?
  a John Adams
  b Maude Adams
  c Jane Addams

11 Who was Henry the Eighth's first wife?
  a Anne Boleyn
  b Catherine Howard
  c Catherine of Aragon

12 The violet is the national emblem of which country?
  a Spain
  b Greece
  c Italy

13 Henry L. Stimson was Secretary of War under President Franklin D. Roosevelt, President Truman and which other President?
  a Taft
  b Wilson
  c Coolidge

14 The first subway was opened in:
  a London
  b Boston
  c New York

15 Which is the largest planet?
  a Mercury
  b Jupiter
  c Saturn

12. TRUE OR FALSE

No. 1

1 Milk is heavier than cream.

True
False

2 Voltaire is a pen name.

True
False

3 Mont Blanc is in Switzerland.

True
False

4 The legs of a colt do not grow longer.

True
False

5 Mice grow into rats.

True
False

6 Los Angeles is a seaport.

True
False

7 Driving a car rapidly uses more gasoline than driving it at a moderate speed.

True
False

8 The Prince Albert coat was named for Prince Albert, consort of Victoria.

True
False

9 A simple fracture is a fracture where only one bone is broken.

True
False

10 Lloyds of London was named after its founder, George Lloyd.

True
False

11 The Kaiser's arm was injured during World War I.

True
False

12 Diamonds burn.

True
False

13 The female mosquito does not bite.

True
False

14 Drowning persons rise to the surface three times.

True
False

15 1900 and 1932 were leap years.

True
False

16 A snake swallows its own skin.

True
False

17 In U.S. California has the longest coastline.

True
False

18 Boxing day celebrates the famous pugilistic match between Fitzpatrick and Sullivan.

True
False

19 A printer's devil is an apprentice printer.

True
False

20 A naturalized citizen cannot be deported.

True
False

No. 2

1 More snow falls in Virginia than in the Arctic
   lowlands.   True
                                              False

2 Quicksand is simply a loose mass of sand
   mixed with water.   True
                                              False

3 Lightning never strikes twice in the same
   place.   True
                                              False

4 Homing pigeons have to be trained to return
   home.   True
                                              False

5 Wolves run in packs.
                                              True
                                              False

6 Bats can fly in total blackness because of
   their keen hearing.   True
                                              False

7 After a bee has stung a human, the bee will
   die.
                                              True
                                              False

8 Rigor mortis sets in within ten minutes after
   death.
                                              True
                                              False

9 Drowned women always come to the top of
   the water face upwards.
                                              True
                                              False

10 It gets colder in Montana than it does at the
   North Pole.
                                              True
                                              False

13. LITERARY QUIZ

1 Who wrote the famous story, dealing with the supernatural, entitled *The Turn of the Screw?*

2 Who was the first Poet Laureate of England?

3 In what works are the following characters to be found? (a) Eppie, (b) Captain Absolute, (c) Sir Toby Belch, (d) Sampson Brass.

4. Name five plays by Shakespeare in which a character named Antonio appears.

5 Whose story links together the tales of *The Arabian Nights?*

6 How did Barkis, in David Copperfield, propose marriage to Clara Peggotty?

7 Who wrote *The Cloister and the Hearth?*

8 What are the Dramatic Unities?

9 Complete the following: (a) Damon and_____,

  (b) Daphnis and _____, (c) Darby and

_____.

10 In what famous battle in England was the *Song of Roland* sung?

11 What was the "Siege Perilous"?

12 Who wrote *A Dissertation on Roast Pig?*

13 What was Brook Farm?

14 Who wrote *Paradise Regained?*

15 What was the name of Don Quixote's servant?

14. QUIZ ON WORLD WAR II

1 When was the atomic bomb dropped on Hiroshima?

2 When did Great Britain declare war on Germany?

3 What was the name of the German battleship scuttled outside of Montevideo?

4 On what date did the Germans enter Paris?

5 Who were the Japanese envoys who conferred with

President Roosevelt and Cordell Hull just before Pearl Harbor?

6 On what date did Germany invade Russia, without a declaration of war?

7 What were the names of the two English ships sunk in the Pacific on December 10, 1941?

8 On what date did Corregidor surrender, and who was in command at the time?

9 What was the name of the Czechoslovakian village that was wiped out completely, because "it assisted the murderers of Heydrich"?

10 What Frenchman took over authority in French Africa and was subsequently murdered?

11 Who succeeded Mussolini as premier of Italy?

12 When was D-Day?

13 Where did the United States-British-Soviet peace security conference first meet?

14 On what date did Germany surrender?

15 On what day did Japan surrender?

15. SCIENCE QUIZ

1 What are the principal constituents of the earth's atmosphere?

2 To what cause is the Aurora Borealis now ascribed?

3 What causes deserts?

4 In what parts of the world do the greatest number of hurricanes occur?

5 Why does ice float on water?

6 What is the average temperature of the sea?

7 What causes rainbows?

8 How do stalactites and stalagmites differ?

9 Name at least four good conductors of electricity.

10 What is the purpose of using fuses?

11 Will water boil more quickly in a polished tea kettle or in a dull-surfaced tea kettle? Why?

12 Will a body weigh more at the equator than at the poles?
13 Define a light year.
14 What is the Zodiac?
15 Next to the diamond, what is the hardest known mineral?

16. GEOGRAPHICAL QUIZ

1 Name three state capitals whose names begin with the same letter as the state.
2 Name five state capitals whose names begin with the letter "A."
3 What general principle governs the numbering of United States automobile highway routes?
4 What chief discovery was made by each of the following men: Captain Cook, da Gama, Peary?
5 To what part of the earth is the name America applied? In whose honor was it named?
6 Where are the following National Parks located: Crater Lake, Glacier, Lassen Volcanic, Rocky Mountain, Mount Rainier, Sequoia and Yellowstone?
7 What are the names of the New England states?
8 Is the area of Canada greater or smaller than that of the United States?
9 What was the approximate population of New York City in 1940?
10 From what country did the United States buy Alaska?
11 Name twelve cities beginning with the letter "M" outside of the United States which have populations of 500,000 or more.
12 What states of the Union never held the status of territories?

13 What were the original thirteen States?
14 Name the three longest rivers in the world.
15 What state was set aside in 1834 as Indian Territory by the United States?
16 What city was named by flipping a coin?
17 What state in the United States touches only one other state?
18 Where could a house be built to have all four corners in a different state?
19 In what state is Boulder Dam?
20 Name the capital of Australia.

17. MUSICAL QUIZ

1 Name the composer who wrote twenty operas, forty-one symphonies, and numerous other works. He died at the age of thirty-five.
2 What well-known writer of musical comedies wrote what well-known college song?
3 What famous composer wrote his first symphony when he was in his forties?
4 Cardinal Newman, English convert to Catholicism, wrote the words of a very famous hymn. Can you name the hymn?
5 Can you name the famous sentimental song for which Sir Arthur Sullivan, collaborator of Gilbert, wrote the music?
6 Edna St. Vincent Millay wrote the libretto for an opera produced at the Metropolitan. Can you name it?
7 For what instrument did Chopin write chiefly?
8 Around what fairy tale did Humperdinck write a famous opera?
9 What is the meaning of the term "chamber music"?
10 Who is the father of modern music?

18. MATHEMATICAL QUIZ

1 What is a unit?
2 What is a factor?
3 What are addends?
4 Reduce the fraction 6/8 to fourths.
5 How many thirds are there in 16-2/3?
6 Add 2/3 and 3/4.
7 Distinguish between long and short division.
8 Draw a right-angled triangle.
9 Six dollars is 30 per cent of how many dollars?
10 If a player makes six hits in 24 times at bat, what is his per cent of hits?

19. GENERAL QUIZ

1 Does a whippoorwill sing while he is on the ground?
2 Who originated the word "cent" for the American penny?
3 How did the name *bootlegger* originate?
4 How much silver does German silver contain?
5 What is a bucket shop?
6 Where was Julius Caesar killed?
7 What is the traditional and unofficial motto of the United States Postal Service?
8 What country's flag has endured longest without change?
9 How did the barber pole originate?
10 What Queen of England was never in England?

Ice Breakers

1. PHANTOM NUMBERS

Long before the game begins, you and your confederate make secret preparations. These consist of marking the figures 1089 in soap on your confederate's bare arm. When the soap marking dries it becomes invisible. Subsequently, you give a member of the party a piece of paper and pencil and ask him to write three digits, the last of which is two less than the first, such as: 987. Then you ask him to reverse these numbers, which are unknown to you. In this case the numbers would read: 789. Then ask him to subtract the reversed number from his chosen number: 987 minus 789. The remainder is, of course, 198. Now ask him to reverse these digits and add the result to the number he had before reversing them (891 plus 198). The total will always be 1089. The calculator is asked to remember his result and the slip of paper on which the total is written is folded carefully, so that the conductor of the experiment cannot see the written numbers. The conductor then burns the paper to ashes. When the ashes cool, the conductor picks them up, and rubs them on the arm of his unknown accomplice on the spot which has been marked in soap. The figures 1089 will then stand up in dark relief.

2. CARD TRICK

This is an ancient card trick originally worked out in Latin and later translated into English. It is an excellent trick, impossible to detect, no matter how many times you do it for your audience. Yet it is simple to perform.

Take twenty cards from a regular deck. Any twenty

will do. Now, lay them out face up, two at a time with every card showing, so that they look like this:

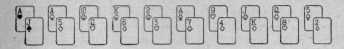

Ask your audience mentally to choose one of the ten pairs. In this case one might choose the Ace of Hearts and Jack of Spades. All the people who are watching may choose a pair. After this is done, gather up the cards, being sure to keep all of the pairs, such as the Ace of Hearts and the Jack of Spades, together, but otherwise picking them up haphazardly. Now, comes the trick. The key to it is the following four words:

        T H I G H
        A T L A S
        G O O S E
        B I B L E

After glancing at these words you will note that each word has a letter repeated in it (the H repeated in Thigh, the A in Atlas, etc.), as well as one letter that appears once in the other three words. (The I in Thigh is also in Bible, the G in Thigh is also in Goose, etc.) You must memorize these words in the order shown. These words set the pattern for your laying out of the cards for the second time for your audience. The first time you laid out the cards, you put them in twos. Now the second time, you use the letters in the four given words and lay out the cards face up, in the following manner:

You put five cards across the first and every row thereafter, as there are five letters in each of the words and make four rows for the number of words used in the key. Now, as you start putting down the cards you must mentally spell out the key words. The first card will cover the T in Thigh; the second card must cover the T in Atlas, the third card will cover the H in Thigh and the fourth card will cover the other H in Thigh, the fifth card will cover the I in Thigh and the sixth card will cover the I in Bible. In other words, every time you cover a letter in the mentally spelled words, you must cover its corresponding letter in the same word or in one of the other words with a card. To illustrate, the moves are numbered:

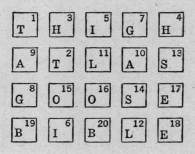

After you have laid out the twenty cards for the second time, you ask your audience, one by one, what row or two rows their chosen pair of cards appear in. If, for example, they say the first and second row, you know the only letter that appears in the first row and also in the second row is T. So you know the pair they have chosen covers the T's in your mental diagram. If they say both cards appear in the first row, then the cards they have chosen are covering the H's in Thigh and so on throughout the diagram. It is really a baffling trick for an audience, and we hope you have fun fooling them.

3. A GOOD BET

The following trick is very deceiving. If you try to make bets on it, your friends will snatch at the chance, but will regard you as slightly wacky. However, the odds—much to everyone's surprise—are decidedly in your favor. You take two well-shuffled decks of cards. Give one to your friend and keep the other for yourself. Now you bet him that you can each turn a card simultaneously and some place in the deck you and he will turn up the identical card. Don't blame us if you fail once, for the odds are still in your favor.

4. EGG IN THE BOTTLE

You can amaze your friends by betting them that you can insert a peeled hard boiled egg through the neck of a milk bottle and into the bottle itself without breaking the egg. Let them try it first to discover how impossible it seems. You then show them how it is done.

Take a piece of paper and set it on fire. Drop it into the bottle. While the paper is still burning, take the egg and set it in the neck of the bottle. You will be amazed yourself to see it drop through gently.

5. QUICK ADDITION

This is a mathematical trick. Nothing could be simpler to perform, but it is difficult to detect.

Ask your audience to write down two rows of figures, five digits in each row, such as:

$$8, 7, 6, 5, 3$$
$$3, 6, 9, 8, 7$$

Now you (the performer) add a third row of figures. Ask your audience to write a fourth, and you write the fifth and last. As soon as you have finished writing the fifth line, you can tell your audience the sum of the written figures. It will take them time to add it up in order to prove your lightning calculations correct.

Here is how it is done: When you write the third and fifth rows of figures, you put down figures that will total nine, when added to the numbers just above them. It will look like this.

YOUR GUEST: 87653
YOUR GUEST: 36987
YOU: 63012 (Note: You've made each
                                          number add up to
                                          9 with the second
                                          row.)

YOUR GUEST: 56481
YOU: 43518 (again totaling nine with
                         ———   row above)
TOTAL: 287651

You get your grand total, instead of adding as your audience will do, by subtracting two from the right-hand number of the first line—it is three in this case—and putting two in front of the first figure in the first line.

6. WHAT'S YOUR AGE?

By performing this ingenious trick you will appear to be a mathematical wizard to your unknowing friends. Ask anyone in the room whose age you do not know to write down his telephone number and carefully conceal it from you. Let us assume that he has written: REGENT 4-6230. Now have him transpose these numbers any way he pleases—for example: 32604. Then he substracts the smaller from the larger of these two numbers: 46230 .

$$\begin{array}{r} 46230 \\ \underline{32604} \\ 13626 \end{array}$$ Then he adds the five digits of

his result: $1 + 3 + 6 + 2 + 6 = 18$. If the total has two or more digits, he must continue to add these digits until he arrives at only one digit. In this case: $1 + 8 = 9$. The next step is to ask him to add 7 to his total, making, in this instance, $9 + 7 = 16$. The last step is for him to add the last two digits of the year in which he was born. When this step is completed, he announces the total for the first time. Let us assume that the year of his birth was 1915. $15 + 16 = 31$. By mentally subtracting 16 from the announced total, you ascertain the year of birth. Because you wish to give his age and not the year of his birth, you announce the result of your mental subtraction as his correct age.

The explanation of this trick is simple. When you take any number, transpose it and subtract the smaller from the larger, the answer will be nine or a combination of digits which, when added, will total 9. Adding seven to this result always gives sixteen, obviously. When you subtract 16 from the total he has announced —namely, the last two digits of the year of his birth plus 16—the result must be the last two digits of the year of his birth.

7. I CAN DO THIS, BUT I CAN'T DO THAT

This is a trick game. You tell your guests that you are going to do something which you are sure they will not be able to do. You then clear your throat audibly but unobtrusively, and pat out a simple rhythm with one hand, either on a table or the floor, to accompany these spoken words: "I can do this, but I can't do that." When you have finished, ask your guests to try it. They will try to imitate your rhythm without realizing that the trick is to clear their throats first. You may perform the trick for them as many times as you choose or until they discover the prank.

8. COLLABORATION

Two people must collaborate on this trick, but no one else should be aware of the alliance. One of the two leaves the room while the remaining guests choose one member of their group whom the absent man must name when he returns to the room. He looks around the room carefully and then points to the man who is picked by the group. Everyone gasps in wonder at this evidence of mental telepathy.

The trick is very simple. No two people sit in exactly the same position. The collaborator assumes the exact sitting position of the man or woman chosen. Naturally, he changes his position if the chosen person moves. If the unknown collaborator is chosen, he assumes a position unlike any other in the room.

9. SPELLING TRICK

Ask a person how he spells JOKE. He spells it for you and then you say, "How do you spell POKE?" When he has spelled it, say "How do you spell the white of an egg?" Invariably he says, YOKE. Obviously this is doubly wrong. The white of an egg is not YOKE. Nor is it YOLK. It is ALBUMEN.

10. ANIMAL CLUES

This trick is done with an ally. One of the allies—let us say it is you—goes out of the room while a name is chosen. It can be a famous name or the name of one of your guests. You then return to the room and your ally starts questioning you:

> ALLY: "Is it Mary Pickford?"
> YOU: "No."
> ALLY: "Is it Bugs Baer?"
> YOU: "No."
> ALLY: "Is it Anne Shirley?"
> YOU: "Yes."

The clue you received: The name *before* that of the chosen name is an animal name (in this case it was Baer—or bear). You can do this trick over and over without having the clue detected. A few animal names are listed below which may be used as clues: Thomas Wolfe, Charles Lamb, Ursula Parrott, Admiral Byrd. It is wise, when repeating the trick, to choose a different animal name each time.

11. GEOGRAPHICAL CLUES

You need a cohort in this game, too. You leave the room. While you are out a famous name is chosen. Let us say John Barrymore. When you return, your cohort gives you the name in the following way:

Using the vowels   A   E   I   O   U
                as   1   2   3   4   5   he says:

"I went to Pittsburgh, then to Rochester, where I stayed four days. I left there and went to Frankfurt, where I stayed three days. It was pleasant there, but I always like London. So I went there and stayed two months."

Using the first letter of the towns he gave you: P for Pittsburgh, R for Rochester (he stayed there four days, so next comes O), then F for Frankfurt. He stayed there three days, so you add I, then to L for London, and for two months add an E. It spells out PROFILE. John Barrymore was known as the Profile, so you say "John Barrymore," to the astonishment of your audience.

The audience, in looking for clues in the spelling, will naturally keep an ear tuned for the letters in Barrymore's name. Your cohort must always find something the chosen name is associated with, such as:

> Chamberlain —Umbrella.
> Sinatra   —Voice
> La Guardia   —The Little Flower.
> Ann Sheridan—Oomph.

12.   WHAT'S IN THE CARDS*

For centuries playing cards have been used as a means of telling fortunes, and many methods of reading their meaning have been developed and passed down from generation to generation.

GENERAL INSTRUCTIONS

It is not considered lucky to read the cards alone. Two persons are required for this. The one who wishes to have his fortune told is known as the *Questioner*. The one who assists him by reading the meaning of the cards is referred to in the following pages as the *Seer*.

In cutting the cards the Questioner should always use the left hand.

Before the reading begins the Questioner usually has to select a card which will represent him, and which is known as the Questioner's card. If the Questioner is dark-haired, with dark eyes and dark complexion, the King of Spades is usually chosen to represent a man and the Queen of Spades a woman. The King and Queen of Clubs represent, according to sex, the Questioner who has brown hair and brown eyes. Questioners

* From "Fortune Telling For Fun and Popularity" by Paul Showers. Copyright, 1942, by Garden City Publishing Co., Inc.

with blue or gray eyes and light brown hair are represented by the King and Queen of Hearts, according to sex, while with blond Questioners, the Queen of Diamonds represents the women and the King of Diamonds the men.

THE DECK OF 32 CARDS

After the lower cards, from twos through sixes, have been discarded from the regulation pack, the remaining thirty-two cards must be marked so as to indicate the top and bottom of each card. This may be done by putting a light pencil mark in one corner of each card. In this way the Seer will be able to determine at a glance whether the card has been laid down in normal or reversed position. This is most important, for the meaning of the card depends upon whether it appears reversed or not.

THE MEANING OF THE 32 CARDS

CLUBS

ACE—Good luck. Favorable news, possibly that the Questioner will receive money. A letter. *Reversed* —Good news but the happiness will be brief. The correspondence will not be pleasant.

KING—A dark man, loyal friend, honest. *Reversed*— Worry or disappointment, good plans coming to naught.

QUEEN—A dark woman, a friend, full of devotion. *Reversed*—Unreliable, a coquette, jealous.

JACK—Dark young man, bright and amusing, bold and eager in wooing. *Reversed*—He is fickle, a flatterer.

TEN—Good fortune, ease and luxury. *Reversed*—A trifling failure, or travel possibly by air or water.

NINE—Unexpected windfall in the way of money. *Reversed*—A little gift, or some sort of difficulty.

EIGHT—Love from a worthy individual, bringing fortune and happiness. *Reversed*—Unworthy love, bringing trouble. Or papers bringing trouble.

SEVEN—Small money or business affair. *Reversed*—Difficulties over money. An unfavorable omen possibly involving legal matters.

HEARTS

ACE—Pleasant tidings, a love letter, the Questioner's home. *Reversed*—Change of place, a friend's visit.

KING—Fair-haired man, loyal and friendly. *Reversed*—Disappointment connected with this person.

QUEEN—Light-haired woman, dependable and affectionate. *Reversed*—Unhappy love connected with her. She may be fickle.

JACK—Fun-loving young bachelor; possibly a child. *Reversed*—Young man linked with disappointment or unhappiness, possibly a soldier.

TEN—Very favorable. Good luck, happiness. A proposal. Helps to cancel bad cards. *Reversed*—Fleeting trouble, possibly a birth.

NINE—This represents the wish. Also slight troubles, but eventual success. *Reversed*—Fleeting troubles.

EIGHT—Love from a light-complexioned person. Marriage thoughts. *Reversed*—Love that is not returned.

SEVEN—Happy thoughts. *Reversed*—Boredom, ennui, possibly jealousy.

DIAMONDS

ACE—A letter. Marriage offer. *Reversed*—News that brings sorrow.

KING—Man with light hair (possibly gray), may be a soldier. *Reversed*—Deception or treacherousness, possibly connected with him.

QUEEN—Light-haired woman, rather common and vulgar, gossipy. *Reversed*—Difficulties caused by the malice of this woman.

JACK—A young man, an employee, someone in a subordinate position. *Reversed*—He causes trouble, cannot be trusted.

TEN—Journey or change of residence. *Reversed*—Bad luck as a result of the trip or change of residence.

NINE—Trouble coming, worries, annoyances. *Reversed*—Dispute in the family or between lovers.

EIGHT—A love affair. *Reversed*—Disappointment in love, affections spurned.

SEVEN—Teasing, unkind criticism, possibly a child. *Reversed*—A minor scandal or some small slander, based on a trifle.

SPADES

ACE—Satisfaction or pleasure connected with the emotions. *Reversed*—Sorrow or sad news.

King—A dark man, possibly a widower; untrustworthy. *Reversed*—A dangerous foe. The wish to work evil.

Queen—A widow or an older woman. *Reversed*—A woman bent upon evil-doing.

Jack—A young man, possibly a student in law or medicine. An ill-bred young fellow. *Reversed*—A disloyal young man, deceitful and dangerous.

Ten—Misery and sorrow, loss of liberty. *Reversed*—The trouble will be of brief duration.

Nine—A bad omen. News of loss or failure. *Reversed*—Unhappiness for someone close to the Questioner.

Eight—Approaching disappointment. *Reversed*—A love affair or match broken up; dissolute living.

Seven—Anxieties; the making of a new resolution. *Reversed*—Silly scheming in love.

Meaning of Card Groups

4 Aces—Perils, loss of money or honor, separations. If one ace is reversed, these troubles are not so grave; if two are reversed, the danger is further lessened; if all are reversed, it is slight.

3 Aces—Brief anxieties, with good tidings to follow; if all are reversed they foretell a foolhardy action.

2 Aces—Some sort of partnership; the diamond and spade together indicate evil or misfortune to come. Other combinations are favorable. If one of the cards is reversed, the partnership will not be entirely successful. If both are reversed, it will fail.

4 Kings—Advancement, wealth, honor. With each re-

versed card, the good fortune will be less but it will happen sooner.

3 KINGS—Something of great importance is to be started; the more cards that are reversed, the less successful it will be.

2 KINGS—A commercial alliance. One reversed means partial success. Both reversed mean failure.

4 QUEENS—A social affair. The more cards that are reversed, the more the fun will be spoiled by unexpected circumstances.

3 QUEENS—A gathering of friends. With each reversed card there is greater danger of scandal-mongering and trouble.

2 QUEENS—A talk between friends, with secrets given away. One reversed indicates rivals. Both reversed mean trouble for the one who learns the secret.

4 JACKS—A hilarious party. The more cards that are reversed, the wilder the hilarity, with possible trouble as an outcome.

3 JACKS—Trouble among friends, possibly from gossip. With each reversed card there is greater danger of a quarrel leading to blows.

2 JACKS—Loss of some sort, possibly theft. One reversed means the loss will not happen right away. Both reversed mean it will happen very soon.

4 TENS—Exceptionally good luck in store, especially regarding the Questioner's present undertakings. *Reversed*—The more cards that are reversed, the more hazards that must be overcome before success is reached.

3 TENS—Failure and trouble through legal proceedings. With each reversed card the trouble becomes less serious.

2 TENS—A lucky break coming without warning, it may involve a new kind of occupation. One reversed means it will take place very shortly. Both reversed mean some time will elapse before it occurs.

4 NINES—Unexpected occurrences. The more cards that are reversed, the sooner the surprise will come.

3 NINES—A most favorable sign. Increased prosperity, good health, enjoyment of life. Each reversed card represents an additional amount of brief worry and care before the good fortune occurs.

2 NINES—Some sort of success in commercial affairs. If one or both are reversed, this indicates small troubles and anxiety.

4 EIGHTS—New kind of occupation or a short trip. The more cards that are reversed, the sooner this will occur.

3 EIGHTS—The Questioner's thoughts regarding marriage and love. If any one is reversed, it means merely a flirtation.

2 EIGHTS—A short love affair. One reversed means a disappointment in connection with love. Both reversed mean a sadness resulting from the Questioner's previous actions.

4 SEVENS—Foes working in secret against the Questioner. The more cards that are reversed, the more likely their plotting will fail and they will be suitably punished.

3 SEVENS—Unhappiness, or the loss of friends. With each reversed card the unhappiness will be less severe.

2 SEVENS—Love that is reciprocated. One reversed means deception in love. Both reversed mean regrets over love.

MEANING OF SPECIAL COMBINATIONS WITH 32 CARDS

In addition to the above meanings of the individual cards and of groups of the same denomination there are also certain combinations of two or more cards which have special meanings when the pack of 32 cards is used. These are listed below according to the four suits for rapid identification. It should be understood that these meanings apply *only* when the cards listed appear *side by side*.

CLUBS

ACE—When surrounded by *diamonds* or with diamonds not more than one card away from it, the Ace of Clubs signifies money coming to the Questioner. With the *nine of diamonds* it indicates legal business of some sort.

KING—With *ten of clubs*, an offer of marriage is to be expected.

QUEEN—With *seven of diamonds* this Queen indicates an uncertain outcome of events. With *Ace of Spades*, a tiresome journey.

JACK—With *Jack of Spades*, loss of money, unprofitable business ventures.

TEN—With an *ace* of any suit following this indicates a big amount of cash.

NINE—With *ten of hearts* this indicates the stage or screen, possibly a theater. With *nine of hearts* it foretells a will or legacy bringing good fortune to the Questioner. With *eight of hearts* it indicates a good time or celebration.

EIGHT—With *Ace of Diamonds*, money coming unexpectedly. With *ten of diamonds*, a trip in connection with a love affair. With *eight of diamonds*, true love.

SEVEN—With *Jack of Hearts*, a love affair in which one party is more interested in gaining social prestige or financial advantage than in true and unselfish devotion. With *ten of spades*, an omen of misfortune in the future.

HEARTS

ACE—When surrounded by *hearts* or with hearts not more than one card away from it, this indicates the beloved, or domestic bliss.

KING—With *nine of hearts*, a love affair with a happy future.

QUEEN—With *seven of diamonds*, joy coming unexpectedly. With *ten of spades*, a dangerous undertaking.

JACK—With *seven of clubs*, a love affair where one party is motivated by a selfish interest in gaining social prestige or financial advantage.

TEN—With *ten of diamonds*, a marriage ceremony.

With *nine of clubs,* the stage or screen, possibly the theater.

NINE—With *nine of clubs,* a will or legacy bringing good fortune to the Questioner.

EIGHT—With *nine of diamonds,* travel to some distant place. With *eight of diamonds,* the beginning of new and important work. With *nine of clubs,* a good time or celebration.

SEVEN—With *Queen of Diamonds,* happiness overshadowed by jealousy.

DIAMONDS

ACE—When surrounded by *diamonds* this indicates the Questioner will prosper financially in his present occupation. With the *eight of clubs,* money coming unexpectedly. With the *seven* and *Jack of Diamonds,* a telegram or wireless message.

KING—With *eight of spades,* a sudden journey.

QUEEN—With *seven of spades,* success to be found in a small community, rather than in a large city.

JACK—With *Ace* and *seven of diamonds,* see Ace of Diamonds.

TEN—With *ten of hearts,* a marriage ceremony. With *eight of clubs,* a trip in connection with a love affair. With *seven of spades,* a lapse of time caused by a delay.

NINE—With *Ace of Clubs,* legal business of some sort. With *eight of hearts,* travel to some distant place.

EIGHT—With *eight of clubs,* true love. With *eight of hearts,* the beginning of new and important work.

SEVEN—With *Ace* and *Jack of Diamonds*, see Ace of
Diamonds. With *eight of spades*, the need to ask
for help. With *Queen of Clubs*, an uncertain outcome of events. With *Queen of Hearts*, joy coming
unexpectedly.

SPADES

ACE—With *Queen of Clubs*, a tiresome journey.

KING—With *seven of clubs*, caution necessary in connection with investments.

QUEEN—With *Jack of Spades*, the Queen signifies a
woman of most evil intentions.

JACK—See Queen of Spades.

TEN—With *Queen of Hearts*, an exciting venture.

NINE—With *Jack of Diamonds*, the advice of friends
should not be accepted too readily.

EIGHT—With *King of Diamonds*, a sudden journey.
With *seven of diamonds*, the need to ask for help.

SEVEN—With *ten of diamonds*, a lapse of time caused
by a delay. With the *King, Queen* or *Jack of
Spades*, this indicates a traitor posing as a loyal
supporter.

MISCELLANEOUS

When a *heart* card of any sort follows a King or
Queen of any one of the suits, that King or Queen
represents someone who wants to be a close friend of
or in love with the Questioner.

If a King, Queen or Jack has cards of the same number on either side (as *eight, Jack, eight,* or *Ace, King,*

Ace), it is a sign of caution to the person for whom the King, Queen or Jack stands.

When the Ace, King, Queen and Jack of one color fall in that order, a wedding is indicated. If the *seven of clubs* is not more than two cards away from this sequence, the couple will have to face financial problems.

A number of *spades* in a row is a sign of misfortune.

A number of *hearts* in a row is a sign of more than one love match, also social gatherings and domestic joys.

A number of *clubs* in a row is a sign of success and happiness.

A number of *diamonds* in a row is a sign of money transactions, usually benefiting the Questioner.

THE DEAL

Here is a very old and reliable method. The Questioner shuffles thoroughly the thirty-two-card pack, then cuts them with the left hand into two sections. From the upper section the Seer removes the bottom card and from the lower section he removes the top card. These two cards he puts aside, face down. They are known as the Surprise.

The Seer then places the lower section on top of the upper section. From this pack of thirty cards he deals off three piles of ten cards each, starting from the right and dealing to the left.

The pile on the left is known as the Past; the pile in

the center is the Present, and the pile on the right is the Future.

The Seer now deals out the ten cards of the Past in a row from left to right, and proceeds to read them. He then does the same with the pile of the Present and the pile of the Future. Last he turns over the two cards of the Surprise. They represent a sudden turn of affairs which will have a direct bearing on the future success and happiness of the Questioner.

Parlor Games

1. QUOTATIONS OR THE GAME

(For 8 or more people)

"Quotations" or "The Game" was devised by Neysa McMein, the famous artist and enthusiastic player of games. Since the night she presented it on a Long Island week-end party it has been played in countless homes throughout the country. Favorite teams have been organized and signals developed. Television companies have offered Miss McMein a great deal of money to put her version of "The Game" on the air. So far, she has declined their offers. Here is a chance for you to learn the game in its different forms. It is a perfect game for a party of ten or more.

VERSION I

ACTING THE GAME

Two teams are chosen with an equal number on each team.

Each team makes up a list of quotations for the opposing team. (This should be done in separate rooms so that there is no possibility that the opposite team will overhear the quotations selected.)

Each quotation, book, play, or song title should be written on separate pieces of paper, one for each member of the opposing team.

When the lists are completed the teams line up on opposite sides of the room and the game begins:

First, Team No. 1 gives a member of Team No. 2 one of its papers with a quotation written on it.

Second, a Team No. 2 member stands up in front of his own team. The quotation on the slip of paper is for his eyes alone. He reads it (not out loud), in order to be able to convey to his team what it is by acting it out in pantomime.

He may tell his team whether it is a play, song, book, or movie title or a familiar quotation. After that he may not speak. By holding up the correct number of fingers he conveys how many words are in the title or quotation and then indicates which word he is about to act, by holding up one finger for the first word, two fingers for the second word and so forth.

After he has read the quotation the opposing team starts to time him and continues until the other team has guessed the quotation or until time is called. (Usually there is a time limit of three minutes for each quotation.) The time is marked down, and then:

Team No. 2 gives a member of Team No. 1 one of its quotations to act out, while Team No. 2 keeps time.

The game is won by the team which guesses the correct quotations in the shortest period of time.

There is a standard set of signals which makes the game easier. The signals should be known to all players participating in "The Game."

They are as follows:

SMALL-WORDS SIGNAL: For a small word (such as *the*, *and*, *a*, *it*, etc.) the actor points to his right index finger. His team members start calling out small words. When the right one is called the actor points to the person who said it, establishing that it is the correct word and nods his head yes.

PUNNING SIGNAL: Sometimes it is impossible to act out a word, but you can often act out a word that sounds like it. For example: if the word *fray* appeared in the quotation you could signal to your team that you were going to act out a *near* word by pointing to your ear lobe—then act out the word *pray*, which is easy to guess. After the team has guessed the *near* word, the team members then say words that rhyme with it or sound like it, until the actor indicates that his teammates have hit upon the correct word. To assist them, the actor can pretend to unravel the edges of his coat sleeve until someone says "fray" which rhymes with *pray*.

SIGNAL FOR DIVIDING WORDS: Some words are more easily acted out if they are divided into syllables. You signify that you are going to "cut up a word" by making a scissors motion with your fore-finger and third finger.

COME-ON SIGNAL: The Come-on signal is one of the most important for an actor to remember. If your team is getting close to the word you are acting, you must indicate that they keep on along the line they are guessing by giving them the "come-on signal" which is: waving the arm as a cop does to motion traffic to go through. This come-on signal should be used if a team member said "lady" and you were trying to get the team to say "women."

STARTING-OVER SIGNAL: To wipe out a word— to start over when your team is on the wrong track: Shake your head no and use your hands as a baseball umpire does when he calls a baseball player safe . . . cross arms, then open them again.

CORRECT-WORD SIGNAL: When the actor points his finger at the person who has said the correct word, it signifies that that person has guessed the right one.

ACTING OUT THE WHOLE-QUOTATION SIG-NAL: Some quotations may be acted out as a whole instead of acting out each word—to signify to your team you are going to do this make a circle with your arms.

NATIONALITY SIGNAL: Sometimes it is possible to let your team know the nationality of the author of a book or play title, or a quotation. You do this by do-ing a step of the dance of the country.

The actor may not use props, i.e., he may not point

to any object in the room, such as a chair, picture, book, or color, to give his team members a clue. Although the actor may not talk, he must act constantly; just to stand still, looking at his team or repeating the same action when they cannot guess the word from his pantomime will not help his team members arrive at the quotation. The actor must listen carefully to everything his team members say, as they may speak as much as they like and he must help them to guess by giving them come-on signals when they are getting warm.

A PRACTICE GAME

Team No. 1 gives a member of Team No. 2 one of its slips. On it is written: "A rolling stone gathers no moss." Timing is started as soon as the member of Team No. 2 has finished reading the quotation and begins to act. He says, "It is a quotation." Then he holds up six fingers to indicate how many words there are in the quotation. He decides not to bother with the opening article of the quotation, figuring that it is such a well-known quotation that a few key words will quickly suggest the whole proverb to his teammates. He knows that "rolling" is the easiest word to act, so he holds up two fingers, thus indicating that he is about to act out the second word. He proceeds to get down on the floor and roll.

TEAM MEMBER: "Tossing."

ACTOR: Shakes his head "no" and rolls some more.

TEAM MEMBER: "Turning."

ACTOR: Shakes head "no," but gives team member come-on signal, and decides to roll a cigarette. He pantomimes this.

TEAM MEMBER: "Roll."

ACTOR: A more emphatic come-on signal is given,

concentrating it upon the team member who has just said "roll."

TEAM MEMBER: "Is the word roll plural—or does it have an -*ed* ending or something like that?"

ACTOR: Shakes his head "yes."

TEAM MEMBER: "ROLLING."

ACTOR: Shakes his head "yes" and points to the man who has just said "rolling." The actor next decides to act out the word "stone."

ACTOR: Indicates he is going to act out the third word by holding up three fingers.

TEAM MEMBER: Third word.

ACTOR: Shakes head "yes." Picks up some imaginary stones from the floor and throws them.

TEAM MEMBER: "Throw."

ACTOR: Shakes head "no" and indicates by pointing to his hand that it is what he is throwing that is important.

TEAM MEMBER: "What are you doing, is it your hand?"

ACTOR: Shakes head "no" and puts an imaginary something into his hand and throws again.

TEAM MEMBER: "Is it what you are throwing?"

ACTOR: Shakes head "yes" and gives him a come-on signal.

TEAM MEMBER: "Stone."

ACTOR: Points to the team member who has just said "stone" and shakes his head "yes."

TEAM MEMBER: "A rolling stone gathers no moss."

ACTOR: "Right."

The time is marked down and the game continues with Team No. 2 giving Team No. 1 one of its quotations to act out.

VERSION II

ACTING THE GAME

The rules of Version II of "The Game" are identical with those of Version I, with these exceptions:

The hostess makes up one list of quotations, book titles, advertising slogans, etc. before her guests arrive. A list of ten should be sufficient. The guests are divided into two or more teams and adjourn to separate rooms. One member from each team, a captain, comes to the hostess, who is in a center room or hall, and she gives the captains the first quotation from her list. Each captain of the various teams gets the same quotation at the same time, and each goes rushing back to his own team to start acting out the quotation. There is no time limit set; each team must continue on the same quotation until the answer is found. In some instances one team may still be working on quotation No. 1 while another team may have completed the entire list that the hostess had prepared. This version is a race against other teams instead of a race against time. After the first quotation is guessed, the person who guesses it rushes out to the hostess to get the second quotation. This procedure is repeated until the hostess' list is exhausted. The team that finishes the list first wins. The actor must repeat to the hostess the quotation just guessed, so that she may look at her list and give the next quotation in its proper sequence.

VERSION III

DRAWING QUOTATIONS

The purpose and rules are the same as "The Game," except that players draw pictures to explain their quotations or slogans or titles. For this game it is best to have all teams (there can be as many teams as you have rooms and tables, with five to eight people on each team) doing the same list at the same time, but separately. The hostess should prepare the list beforehand and act as the referee. When the teams are organized, a member of each team goes to the referee, who whispers the title, quotation, or slogan to all of the captains of all the teams. They then rush back to their teammates, tell them the category and start to draw pictures. No letters or numbers may be written. The artist may not speak, but may use the agreed-upon signals—the same ones described in *Acting Quotations*. The person guessing the quotation runs out to the referee and gets the next quotation. The winning team is the one which finishes the list first. Speed and ingenuity are more important than artistic ability. A simple line drawing as the one shown, easily conveyed the poem entitled: "The Boy Stood on the Burning Deck."

It was drawn in this sequence:

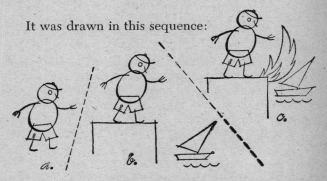

The team guessed man, girl, lady, then boy. The artist signaled "correct," drew the deck and then showed it burning. He kept pointing and encouraging his teammates. When they got "burning" and "boy" they knew the quotation.

2. WHO AM I?

(For 6 or more people)

This is a particularly good game for a party at which the guests do not know each other very well. It will make them mix and begin to converse with all the guests. Before the guests arrive the hostess must prepare slips of paper with famous names written on them —a different name for each guest. When the game begins, the hostess pins one of these famous names on the back of each of her guests. It is then each one's job to discover who he is by asking questions which may be answered only by "yes" or "no." As each guest may read everyone's famous name except his own, it is up to each one to ask one question about himself and then answer one for his informant. Thus it continues, with each guest roaming from person to person, asking a question and answering one until he has established his identity. There is always one person who has difficulty finding out who he is—and it usually ends with the whole group answering his questions to finish the game.

3. WHAT DOES HE REMIND YOU OF?

(For 2 or more players)

In this game one person leaves the room while the group decides on the name of a famous person. In this instance, Joe DiMaggio is chosen. The person who is "it" is called back to try to discover the chosen name. This is arrived at by a series of questions addressed one at a time to each person in the room in regular order until the final answer has been guessed. The questions and answers would go like this:

"IT": What article of clothing does he remind you of?

ANSWER: A baseball suit.

"IT": What part of a newspaper does he remind you of?

ANSWER: Sports section:

The interrogator must realize that the famous person is probably someone in the sports world and most likely plays baseball. So he tries to narrow it down by asking:

"IT": If he were in baseball, what kind of runs would he make?

ANSWER: Home runs.

He guesses Joe DiMaggio and is told he is correct. He may have three guesses, however, if he misses. It is surprising how quickly, through this kind of questioning, the answer is arrived at. Direct questions requiring a "yes" or "no" answer are not allowed; only questions formed with the words "What _____ does he remind you of?"

Sample Questions:

What flower does he remind you of?

What type of furniture does he remind you of?

What perfume does he remind you of? (This question will help you determine the sex of the famous person.)

What newspaper does he remind you of?

What car does he remind you of?

What play does he remind you of?

What movie does he remind you of?

What profession does he remind you of?

The answers to these questions must be fair. If an author is chosen as the famous person and the question "What book does he remind you of?" is asked, you do not have to answer with the title of one of his books. You may answer with the title of any book which describes him and offers a clue to his identity. For example: If the chosen author were Lin Yutang, you could answer, *Oil for the Lamps of China*.

4. IN SEARCH OF A NAME
(For 8 to 12 people)

One amateur detective (two if you have twelve guests) is required for this game. Let us suppose you are entertaining twelve people, including the host and hostess. You send two people out of the room and those remaining form a circle and select a famous name. As there are ten people in the circle it must be a name with ten letters, such as WASHINGTON. (If there were eight people in the circle a name with eight letters would be chosen, etc.) Now each person in the circle is assigned a letter of the name WASHINGTON by going clockwise around the circle. The first person is given W, the person on his left A, and so on until the name is spelled out in its correct order. Now each member of the circle must think of a famous person whose last name begins with the letter assigned to him and be prepared to tell the detectives all they want to know about that person without mentioning his name. The detectives are called in and the game begins. The detectives should make a chart for themselves something like this:

Lewis	*Mary*	*Edith*	*Alice*	*Mac*
W				
Pres. of	Beautiful			
School	Women			
Governor	Horses			

The detectives then ask where the spelling starts and ask the man (Lewis—in this case) to start telling them about his person. Lewis, who was assigned the letter "W," has chosen Woodrow Wilson and starts to talk in this manner:

"I became president of one of the schools that I attended as a young man. I ran for governor of my state and was elected. I introduced many social reforms and gained national recognition because of this. I was an idealist, and though I fought for the things I believed in, I failed to win my most important battle for the people of America. Many say that the chaotic condition of the world today is partly my fault. I believe this is all I will tell you right now."

As you can see by the chart, the detectives have made notes of the information given them by Lewis. They have decided, after consultation, that Lewis is Wilson and have marked a tentative W in the space for the first letter. (If they do not guess Washington by the time they complete the circle, Lewis must give them more information about Woodrow Wilson.) Then the detectives go on to Mary, who is the second in the circle with the letter A. She has chosen Elizabeth Arden as her famous person and says:

"I am a woman who is not envious of beautiful women. As a matter of fact, I try to make even the homely ones pretty. I like horses too. I became famous among men around the time of the Kentucky Derby of 1946. Most women have known me for years and many of them carry my name printed on some object in their purses. I think that is enough about me for now."

And so it goes around the circle. It is fun for those "in the know" to speculate about the people chosen by their fellow-players. Naturally, these speculations must be silent, so as not to give the detectives a hint.

5. BOTTICELLI

(For 2 or more persons)

If there are four or more players, you may work either individually or in teams of two or three. The game is more fun when played by teams. A letter of the alphabet is chosen and the object of the game is to write down as many famous people as you may think of, living or dead, whose first and last names begin with the chosen letter.

Take a large sheet of paper and write the alphabet down the left-hand side of the page. Repeat the alphabet down the middle of the sheet. Now let us suppose the chosen letter is R. The following diagram will show you how your sheet will look.

R

A.	**A**lbertina **R**asch	R.	**R**oger **A**scham
B.	**B**asil **R**athbone	R.	**R**obert **B**urns
C.	**C**harles **R**eade	R.	**R**uth **C**hatterton
D.	_____ R_____	R.	_____ D_____

On the left-hand side of the page, you must write down a famous person whose first name begins with A and whose last name begins with R, as for example Albertina Rasch. Then a person whose first name begins with B and whose last name begins with R, such as Basil Rathbone, and so on down the alphabet. No name may be repeated. If, for instance, you have used Franklin Roosevelt under F, you may not use Theodore Roosevelt or any other Roosevelt in this game. When you have completed as many names as you can think of, shift to the other side of the page and write down a famous person whose first name begins with R and whose surname begins with A, such as Roger Ascham. Next, write down a person whose first name begins with

R and whose surname begins with B, such as Robert Burns, and so on down the alphabet again. Again no name may be repeated. As you have used Robert Burns under B, no other Robert may be used in this game. When you come to the letter R, a famous person whose first and last names begin with R must be used in both columns, such as Rosalind Russell and Richard Rodgers.

A time limit is set, usually about thirty minutes, and when time is up, the names are read out in alphabetical order. If you or your team has a name which no other team has you score five points for that name. If one other team has the same name you each score three points, and if more than two teams have the same name you each score one point. Naturally the more unusual names score the highest points, but the person *must* be well enough known to be identified by all the players. You will find the tantalizing part of the game is the elusiveness of the famous person's first name when you try to set him down on the sheet.

Do not work too long on any one letter that stumps you. Fill in as many names as you can in the time allowed and then if you have extra time go back and try to better them.

6. COFFEE POT

(For 4 or more people)

One person is chosen to leave the room, and the remaining players agree upon one verb which the contestant is to guess when he returns. His method of guessing is to ask each person, in rotation around the room, a question which may only be answered by "yes" or "no." His form of asking the question is to interpolate the word coffee pot into the sentence instead of the missing verb. Let us suppose the verb chosen is "walk." The questioner might ask the first player "Do you coffee pot in the morning?" If the answer is "yes," he might try to establish if the verb is something which is done continuously or only at a certain part of the day. He might then ask "Do you coffee pot with your hands?" "Do you coffee pot with your feet?", etc., and try to establish where the action takes place. By these series of leading questions he should be able to name the verb. Then another contestant leaves the room to continue the game. The more pertinent the questions, the sooner the contestant will arrive at the answer.

7. ADVERBS
(For 4 or more players)

One person is chosen to leave the room and one adverb is picked which the contestant must guess when he returns to the room and asks questions. Let us suppose the adverb to be "austerely." No matter what question is asked each player should answer in a cold frigid tone of voice. His answer should be short and curt, and his posture rigid. If, for example, the first player is asked "Do you like this party?" his answer might be "No. It's much too informal and noisy." The questioner must guess the adverb from the players' answers *and* actions. This game can be great fun and give thwarted actors and actresses a chance to practice their histrionics in the parlor. When the adverb is guessed another player leaves the room and the game continues.

8. GUGGENHEIM
(For 2 or more people)

Each person draws a diagram like the one shown below. The hostess calls out a set of five categories. For example, among the countless categories possible, she might choose the following five: comic-strip characters, magazines, automobiles, authors, Presidents. These are entered by each participant at the left-hand side of the diagram (see sample). Then the hostess gives a five-letter word (such as *March*) or a series of five letters (*g n i e r*). These letters are entered at the top of the diagram, one letter over each line of squares. Time is called and each player is on his own. He or she must fill in the squares in this manner:

CATEGORIES	M	A	R	C	H
Comic-Strip Characters	Caspar Milquetoast				Henry
Magazines	Mademoiselle		Reader's Digest		
Automobiles	Mercury	Austin		Cadillac	
Authors	Marquand				
Presidents	Madison			Coolidge	Hoover

Under the letter M, players must write the name of a comic-strip character whose last name begins with M, a magazine beginning with M, etc. Players are allowed ten minutes. Scoring is as follows: If there are four players in the game, each player gets four points for every word in his diagram which no other player has. If two players have the same word in a square, each gets three points. If three players have the same word in the square, each gets two points, and if everybody has it, it is worth only one point for each. If there are five players, the top score is five, and so on up to eight.

9. WORD SQUARES

(For 2 to 6 players)

It is a perfect drawing-room, beach or train game for adults. The purpose of the game is to build small cross-word puzzles. Each player makes a five-by-five diagram, as shown below:

PLAYER No. 1   *PLAYER No. 2*

G	R	O	B	N
R	A	N	G	E
I	N	T	E	R
N	C			
D	H			

B	R	I	N	G
L	O	V	E	R
O	P	E	N	O
W	E	S	T	U
S	D	T	A	P

A few seconds are then allowed for the players to make a tentative plan (small letters) of words which they are going to try to fit into the puzzle. Then each player calls out a letter in turn. Every player puts the called letter where it will help make complete words. Let us suppose that player No. 1 first calls out "G" (large lettering) with the thought of making the top row of squares the word (GROWN) in his puzzle. Player No. 2 might fit the "G" into his tentatively planned BRING in his top row, and then call out "B." This might make player No. 1 change his planned GROWN to GRABS, so that he may fit the letter "B" into his puzzle. Player No. 1 then calls "R" and player No. 2 calls "I," etc. Constant revision of possible words becomes necessary. Letters called must remain where they are originally placed. When all squares are filled, papers are exchanged and graded. Five points are scored for each completed five-letter word, four points for each completed four-letter word, three points for each completed three-letter word and two points for each completed two-letter word, counted vertically, horizontally, and diagonally. The player who scores the greatest number of points wins.

A more difficult version of this game requires seven, eight or more squares vertically and horizontally. The scoring is based upon the number of squares employed. Thus, for an eight-square game, the maximum score for a word of eight letters would be eight points.

10. CAMOUFLAGE THE OBJECT

(For 4 or more people)

Five or more objects are chosen to be hidden, and shown to all players. Objects might be:

Wedding Ring	Rubber Band
Postage Stamp	Match
Thimble	Penny
Lump of Sugar	Key
Hairpin	Earring
Paper Clip	Button

After the rest of the players have left the room, one person hides the objects. No object may be covered. It must be placed so that it is in plain view and yet deceives the searcher. The paper clip, for instance, may be concealed in a glass of water, but must not be hidden in a closed cigarette box. Each player receives a list of the hidden objects, and starts his search. The players may look wherever they like, but nothing in the room may be moved or touched. When a player finds an object, he should move away from it (so he will

not give the other players any clues) and then jot down
on his list where he has seen the hidden object. The
winner is the player who finds all of the objects first.

The trick in hiding the objects is simple. Place each
object on a spot that more or less matches its own
color. The penny on copper or brass, the thimble on top
of a lamp covering the finial, and a postage stamp
glued onto a liquor bottle over the revenue stamp.

11. PASS THE ORANGE

(For 8 or more players)

"Pass the Orange" is a silly game, but it can provide
a lot of fun.

Two teams are chosen, and each team forms a
circle. The hostess gives each team captain an orange,
which the captains place under their chins. The object
of the game is to pass the orange around the circle
without the use of hands. Obviously, the only way to
accomplish this is for each player to use his chin and
neck as a means of manipulating the orange. After one
player has the orange under his chin, it is up to the
person standing next to him to take it from him by
means of his chin and neck. If the orange drops to the
floor, it must be given to the captain, who starts it
around the circle again. The team which completes the
circuit first wins the game.

12. PASS THE HAT

(For a large number of people)

It is great fun and has never been known to overtax
the mind.

The number of players able to participate at one time
is determined by the number of hats available. One

person is selected to be the caller. He remains bare-headed throughout, but is nevertheless an integral part of the game. The remaining players choose hats, place them on their heads, and form a circle around the caller. The game starts with the caller counting, "Right One." At this call each player places his right hand on the hat of his neighbor to his right. When the caller counts "Two" each player removes his neighbor's hat and places it on his own head. If a player fails to cover his own head on the count of two, he and his hat drop out of the game. The others continue. The tempo of the game depends on the caller, and should be increased after the first few calls. To add to the confusion, the caller may, at any time during the game, call "Left One." This means that the player must change to his left hand, and place it on the hat of his neighbor to the left. If he fails to change in time and removes the wrong hat, he must retire from the game. The words "right" or "left" are only used to start the game, and to indicate a switch. Otherwise the caller merely uses the counts of "one" and "two."

13. MURDER

(For 8 or more players)

The most famous game of "Murder" was played on a gay week-end party, when one of the guests was mur-dered on a Saturday morning—and had to play dead until the murderer was discovered late Sunday night. She has refused all offers for the game *and* week-ends ever since.

The game begins with the hostess taking out as many cards from a deck as she has guests, but being sure to include the Queen of spades and the ten of diamonds among her selected cards. The cards are shuffled and placed face down on a table. Each person draws a card and conceals it from the other players. Whoever draws the Queen of spades has now become the murderer and whoever draws the ten of diamonds is now the detective. The detective announces himself; the murderer keeps an ominous silence. The detective leaves the room (just in case he might get murdered by mistake) and the lights go out in the living room. Everybody mills around the room until the murderer picks his victim, whom he indicates by clasping him lightly around the throat. The victim may not move from that spot, but allows the murderer thirty seconds to get away before he lets out a piercing scream and drops to the floor. The victim's part in the game is over, for from now on until the murderer is detected, he cannot talk or move. The lights go on and the detective returns to the room to start his sleuthing.

Every player in the game must answer questions absolutely truthfully, with the exception of the murderer, who may lie as much as he chooses. His identity is as much a puzzle to the other players as it is to the detective. With questions such as the sample list below, it is amazing how quickly the murderer can be found.

Were you near the victim when he fell?

Did anyone brush by you just before you heard the scream?

What direction was he going?

Did he or she wear a tweed coat or a silk dress?

Did you smell perfume near the victim?

How far have you moved since the victim fell?

If the detective accuses three innocent people of being the murderer, the murderer gets off free.

14. CODE LETTERS

(For 2 or more people)

Code Letters can be played to pass the time on a
train and is also an excellent after-dinner parlor game,
giving amateur sleuths a feeling that they would be
able assistants for J. Edgar Hoover.

A code message is chosen that might have been used
by our enemy agents during the war—and the point of
the game is to conceal this message as well as the
player can in a letter or paragraph within a stipulated
number of words. The hostess may choose a code message before her guests arrive and may even prepare a
paper for each guest. It would look like this:

_____   _____   _____   _____ WATCH

_____   _____   FOR   _____   _____

_____   TROOP   _____   _____   _____   _____

_____   _____   _____   _____   _____ BOAT

_____   _____   _____   _____ PASSING

_____   _____   _____   _____   _____

THROUGH   _____   _____   HARBOR   _____

_____   _____   _____   AND   _____   _____

_____   _____   REPORT   _____   _____   _____

_____   _____   _____   _____   _____   _____

_____   _____   TIME   _____   _____   _____

_____.

Each guest receives an identical form and must fill
in each blank space with one word only. The key words
must remain in the places where they have been

written. The cleverest letter or story which conceals these words wins the game.

Your answer might read like this—or might be considerably better.

"Just bought a beautiful WATCH to give John FOR his birthday. His TROOP arrives home on Saturday. I'm meeting him at the BOAT and we will be PASSING your home on the way THROUGH to Bar HARBOR for a well deserved AND welcome vacation. I will REPORT to you more fully when John returns the date and TIME you may expect us."

After a time limit of ten minutes, the papers are exchanged and read out loud. The merits of each are discussed until a winner is decided upon. When played by people of keen wit, the answers can be very amusing.

15. DETECT THE FAMOUS NAME

(For 2 or more players)

One person is chosen to be *it*. Hereafter he will be called the Counsellor. The Counsellor thinks of the name of a famous person. Let us suppose it to be Sinclair Lewis. He announces, "I am a person whose last name begins with L." (The initial of his last name is the only clue that is given at this time.) Now the other player or players start questioning him in this manner:

PLAYER: "Are you a writer?"

The Counsellor then thinks of an author whose name begins with L and says, "No, I am not Longfellow."

PLAYER: "Are you a painter?"

Again the Counsellor thinks of a painter beginning with L and says, "No, I am not Landseer."

The questioning continues along this line. If the Counsellor cannot think of a person called for beginning with the letter L, the group is allowed to ask one free question. The player must have a famous person in mind when he asks the Counsellor a question, and if the Counsellor is unable to answer, the player must give the name he had in mind before a free question may be asked. The free questions might be: "Is he living?" "Is he a man?" "Is he a painter?" etc., which the Counsellor must answer truthfully with a "yes" or "no." Should the question be, "Is he living?" and the answer "Yes," only living persons may be used in questioning by the group and in answering by the Counsellor. If the question, "Is he a man?" is asked and answered "Yes," thereafter only men may be used in the questions and answers. The group gets one free question every time the Counsellor cannot answer.

The Counsellor and the group can only use famous names once. For example: If the player asks, "Are you a prize fighter?" and the Counsellor says, "No, I am not Joe Louis," then when the player again asks, "Are you a prize fighter?" the Counsellor could not answer Joe Louis again. He would have to think of another prize fighter. If he couldn't, he would give up, and the player of the group would say, "I was thinking of Battling Levinsky." Then he would ask a free question. If the question had been, "Are you an author?" and the Counsellor had not been able to think of any author beginning with an L except Sinclair Lewis, then he would have had to say, "Yes, I am Sinclair Lewis." If the player asks, "Are you the author of *Dodsworth?*", the Counsellor would have to answer: "Yes, I am Sinclair Lewis."

16. STINK PINK

(For 2 or more players)

Stink Pink is an old game newly revived. Anyone who can make a simple rhyme can play it. It always provides amusement.

One player thinks of two words which rhyme like: Fan and Tan. Then this player announces how many syllables are in his rhyming words by saying:

"Stink Pink," if his words are of one syllable.

"Stinky Pinky," if his words are of two syllables.

"Stinkity Pinkity," if his words are of three syllables, and "Ge-Stinkity Ge-Pinkity" if his words are of four syllables. After he has announced this, he gives a simple definition of his rhymed words. In the case of Fan and Tan, he might say, "Stink, Pink. Cooler Color." It is then up to the other player or players to guess the rhymed words he had in mind. When the words are guessed, another player makes up a new rhyme, and so on. Some sample STINK PINKS:

PLAYER: "Stink Pink. False Timepiece."

Answer: "Mock Clock."

PLAYER: "Stink Pink. His Majesty's Possessions."

Answer: "King's Things."

PLAYER: "Stinky Pinky. A note and a dog."

Answer: "Letter, Setter."

PLAYER: "Ge-Stinkity Ge-Pinkity. New York. A place to keep liquor."

Answer: "Knickerbocker Liquor Locker."

17. WRITTEN CHARADES

(For 2 or more would-be poets)

This form of charade conceals a word whose sylla-bles, broken up phonetically, must be substituted for

the words "my first," "my second," etc., offered in the
verse submitted for the other participants to guess. The
whole word replaces the "my all" in the charade. A
word may be divided in different ways in the same
charade. For instance "sausage" may be split into "saw"
and "sage," and elsewhere in the verse, into "sauce"
and "age." The complete verse should always have a
certain consistency of idea, but this need not suggest
the answer to be discovered. Clues, other than the
definitions themselves, and often in pun form, may be
included. (It is desirable, too, that verses scan.)

Here is a very simple example:

> I use a first to write a letter;
> A handy blotter makes things better.
> I bend my last to say a prayer
> Or when I sit upon a chair.
> When children buy a lolly-pop
> They take a total to the shop.

The answer is "penny"—"pen" and "knee." So the
charade, when guessed, would read:

> I use a *pen* to write a letter;
> A handy blotter makes things better.
> I bend my *knee* to say a prayer
> Or when I sit upon a chair.
> When children buy a lolly-pop
> They take a *penny* to the shop.

18. SEVENSIES

(For 4 or more people)

Part of the fun of the game is that the person who
has never played it before is told that it is a very simple
game and that he can catch on to the rules as the game

is being played. There is a penalty for not giving the correct response or for speaking out of turn. The penalty may be pennies or some ridiculous consequence of your own choice. The person being initiated usually pays the penalty in order to find out about each one of the following rules.

The game is played by a group seated in a circle. One person starts things off by giving any number under seven, and pointing either to the right or left of himself. The person who gets pointed at says the next consecutive number. This counting out loud continues until someone is obliged to say the number seven. Instead of saying the number seven, he is supposed to clap. Whenever anybody claps, the order of counting is reversed in the circle. This works out so that the man who says "six" hears a clap for seven from the man next to him, and then, because the order of counting has been reversed, has to say "eight."

The tempo is important. The group is the judge of anyone whose reaction is too slow. In learning the game, one finds that one is expected to clap on fourteen. This is because one claps on all multiples of seven. When one reaches seventeen a clap of the hands is required. One must also clap on any number that has seven as its last digit.

It usually requires quite a few penalties to learn how to handle the two numbers twenty-seven and twenty-eight, since a double reverse occurs at this point.

The first man to say the number fifty gets all of the pennies which have been paid for learning the game and is declared the winner.

If anyone makes a mistake at forty-nine, he must pay a larger forfeit. As the counting is begun anew each time a mistake is made, the person who misses has the privilege of starting the count at any number below seven.

19. POKER SOLITAIRE

Incredible as it may seem, twenty-five cards picked at random from a regular deck can be made into five complete poker hands. The authors have tried this well over a hundred times and so far have always completed the hands.

The combinations allowed to make the complete hands are: flushes (all in one suit), straights (a run of five cards in sequence), full house (three of a kind and a pair), straight flush (five cards in sequence in the same suit), or a royal flush (AKQJ10 of the same suit). Such cards as two pairs or four of a kind are not acceptable, as they leave an unrelated fifth card in the hand.

Let us suppose that the twenty-five cards you picked at random were the following:

DIAMONDS: 2, 4, 8, 10, J, Q.
HEARTS: 3, 4, 5, 8, 9, 10.
SPADES: A, 3, 5, 7, J.
CLUBS: A, 2, 5, 6, 7, 9, 10, J.

The first step is to arrange all of the cards into flushes. Now, reduce all flushes to five cards each. In this case we make up the club hand as follows: A, 2, 9, 10, J. The heart hand as follows: 3, 5, 8, 9, 10. The spade hand was complete, and in the diamond hand we left 2, 4, 10, J, Q. The cards we had left over from the flushes were: the four of hearts, the five, six, seven of clubs and the eight of diamonds, which made up a straight for our fifth hand. It is not always so simple, but a little concentration will work it out.

Poker Solitaire can be played as a competitive game by making it either a race against time or a match to decide who can arrange the highest hands.

Parents' Treasury
of CHILDREN'S GAMES

The answer to "Pin the tail on the Animal" will be found on page 208.

1. PIN THE TAIL ON THE ANIMAL

Below are sketches of animals. Their tails and their bodies have been separated—it is up to the child to match the right tail with the right animal.

1 _____   4 _____
2 _____   5 _____
3 _____   6 _____

1. _____ 4. _____
2. _____ 5. _____
3. _____ 6. _____

2. HANGMAN

(For 2 people)

HANGMAN is a very simple game and is fun for any child who can spell, even if he or she knows how to spell only two or three words. A word is chosen and kept secret by one person. The object of this game is for the other participant to discover the chosen word. Let us suppose it to be car. A line is drawn for each letter in the word like this:

_____ _____ _____

a b c d e f g h i j k l m n o p q r s t u v w x y z

The alphabet is written below the lines, as shown. Now, the child begins to guess any one of the twenty-six letters, and as the letters are guessed they are crossed out of the written alphabet. If the guessed letter appears in the chosen word, it is placed in the proper space on the drawn lines. If any letter is called which appears in the word more than once—it is put into its proper place as many times as it appears. A letter may be called only once. If the child guesses a letter which does not appear in the chosen word, one part of the hangman is drawn for each missed letter. If the child does not guess all the letters before the hangman is completed, he has lost the game and a new word is chosen. The hangman is drawn in this sequence.

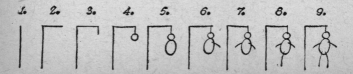

1. 2. 3. 4. 5. 6. 7. 8. 9.

3. DOT BOXES
(For 2 or 4 players)

This is one of the oldest games in the world, but it is amusing for children.

Make a series of as many dots as you choose in straight lines as illustrated.

```
.   .   .   .   .

.   .   .   .   .

.   .   .   .   .

.   .   .   .   .

.   .   .   .   .
```

When the diagram is drawn, the play begins by Player A's drawing one line from one dot to another. Players may draw lines horizontally or vertically, but not diagonally. It is now Player B's turn and he draws a line from a second dot to another, and so on. The object of the game is to capture squares, by adding the fourth line after three sides of a square have been filled in. Each player, upon completing a square or squares, puts his initials into the captured square space or spaces and then draws one more line from one dot to another that does not complete a square. You may complete as many squares on one turn as you can by drawing one line to complete each square. The winner of the game is the person who has his or her initials in the greatest number of squares.

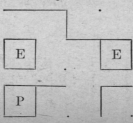

4. ASSOCIATIONS

There are many variations of this game.

a. ASSOCIATIONS FOR YOUNG CHILDREN

You can very easily teach young children to play this game by telling them that you are going to say a word. Let us suppose it is "cat." Then they are to say another word that the word "cat" makes them think of. The associations they make are interesting and amusing. The game, starting with the word "cat" might go something like this:

> Adult: "Cat."
> Child: "Mouse."
> Adult: "Cheese."
> Child: "Sandwich."
> Adult: "Bread."
> Child: "Knife," etc.

Obviously, there can be no winner of this game, but it frequently brings out many revealing and hilarious word-associations.

b. ASSOCIATIONS FOR CHILDREN FROM EIGHT TO FOURTEEN

This game is played in exactly the same manner as Associations for Young Children, with this exception: The adult picks a word—such as *lion*—which becomes the forbidden associated word, the word to be avoided if possible. Now the game starts with any chosen word, and the players try to work the associations around to where some player will have to say *lion*. Using "Lion" as the forbidden association, the adult could get the game over very quickly by starting with "King of the Beasts," as there is only one answer, but it would hardly be fair. However, he could so manipulate his choice

of words that it would come in later in the ASSOCIA-
TIONS.

c. ASSOCIATIONS FOR CHILDREN OF FOURTEEN AND OLDER

This game requires a group of four or more children.
It is played exactly like the game of Associations for
Young Children, with this exception: After each player
has said four Associated words going clockwise around
the group, you start going backwards, saying the same
words that have been said but in reverse. For example,
suppose on the first four rounds the associated words
were: "glasses, eyes, nose, smell, odor, cabbage, corned
beef, Dinty Moore, funny papers, etc." Now, instead of
continuing a fifth round, the person who started the
first associated word must say "Dinty Moore," the person on his or her right must say, "corned beef," etc., going back over the associated words in their reverse
order. A player who cannot think of the correct word
drops out of the game and the player next to him or
her who can remember the correct word continues with
the game. The ones who remember them all in their
proper sequence are the winners.

5. CROSS THE SCISSORS

(For 4 or more players)

CROSS THE SCISSORS is more of a trick than a
game, but it is fun for a limited time. It is for children
and/or adults. To play CROSS THE SCISSORS you
need only a pair of scissors. Any size will do.

The only play in the game is to pass the scissors
around a seated circle of players, from one person to
another. The person passing the scissors, however, must
say how the scissors are passed. There are only two

ways to pass the scissors; one is to pass them *crossed* and the other is to pass them *uncrossed*. The players are not told how to pass them crossed or uncrossed; they must observe this from the players who pass the scissors correctly. After the scissors change hands each player is told whether or not he passed the scissors correctly. The trick is simple. It has nothing to do with the scissors. If you say, "I pass the scissors to you crossed," and you have your legs crossed, you are correct, but if you had your legs uncrossed, your statement would not be correct. As a deliberate act is put on during the passing of the scissors, with much opening and closing of them going on, it is difficult for the players to discover the trick. When most of the players catch on, they cross and uncross their legs obviously to help the remaining unobservant players learn the trick, and thus end the game.

6. STORES

(For 2 or more players)

This is an excellent rainy-day or train game for children. You need as many decks of cards as there are players. Each player takes a deck of cards and decides on the kind of store he or she wants to represent. The players should all choose different stores to add to the confusion. The stores might be: a pet shop, department store, grocery store, hardware store, etc. Now, the game begins:

All the players turn up one card at a time *simultaneously* from their own deck. If any of the players turns up a card that matches any other players turned-up card in suit and number, both players must call out some article that may be bought in the store that the other player has chosen. For example: Let us suppose that Jane has decided to be a pet shop and Jim, who is

also playing, chose a grocery store. Now when Jane
and Jim turn up matching cards, Jane calls out,
"Coffee" or any other item that might be bought in
Jim's grocery store; while Jim calls out, "Dog," an
animal which could be bought in Jane's pet shop. The
one who calls out the article first gives all of the cards
he or she has turned up in front of him or her to the
player who lost in calling articles. The cards given to
the losing caller are put in his turned-up pile in front
of him. The player who gets rid of all of his cards first,
wins the game. When the deck has been gone through,
the player without shuffling the cards turns them over
and starts through them again.

7. MEMORY-TEST

(For 3 or more people)

What you need: a plain tray (though a table top
and a cloth to cover it will do) and twenty-five to
thirty small common household articles, such as:

POWDER	SPOON	HAIRPIN
PUFF	RAZOR	LIPSTICK
THIMBLE	BOX OF	BUTTON
STICK OF	ASPIRIN	TAPE
GUM	NAIL	MEASURE
BOTTLE OF	SCISSORS	SAFETY PIN
INK	PAPER	PACKAGE OF
PENCIL	MATCHES	CIGARETTES
PEN	BOTTLE	PIPE
KEY	OPENER	CIGAR
COMB	SPOOL OF	RING
TWEEZERS	THREAD	TOOTHPICK
NAIL BRUSH	WRIST-	ERASER
BOTTLE CAP	WATCH	

These articles should be irregularly placed on the

table top or tray. Players are allowed to study these articles for three minutes. Then the tray is taken away or the table top is covered. The players must then write down as many articles as they can remember. The one who remembers the greatest number of articles in the allotted time wins.

8. TILLIE

(For 2 or more players)

TILLIE is an excellent game for children, because even after they have discovered the trick, it is fun to play. One person who knows the game starts it by saying: "Tillie loves the moon and hates the sun." The next player tries to figure out why Tillie loves the moon and why she hates the sun and says what he thinks Tillie loves and hates. He is told whether he is right or wrong. The trick is simple. Tillie loves any word with a double letter and hates any word that does not have a double letter. Tillie, for instance, would love pepper and hate salt, love wood and hate a table, etc. There is no winner of the game, but it does provide amusement.

9. GEOGRAPHY

(For 2 or more players)

Geography is an oral game that will make any automobile or train trip seem shorter, and is also fun in the parlor. The players first decide on geographical categories, such as cities, rivers, states, or even all three. If cities are chosen, the first player might call out "Troy." From here on, any city named must begin with the last

letter of the preceding city. In this case the word after
Troy would have to begin with Y. So the second player
might say, "Yonkers." The third player, using the "s"
(the last letter in Yonkers), says: "Scranton," and so
on around the room. In case of two-letter names, such
as Oklahoma City, the "Y" must be used to begin the
next word. No names may be repeated. When a player
cannot think of a city beginning with the last letter of
the preceding city, he drops out of the game. The letter
he missed is taken by the next player in line, and so
it continues until there is only one player left, who is
the winner.

10. CAR POKER

(For 2 or more people)

Car Poker is an excellent game for breaking the
monotony of a long motor trip. License plates on passing automobiles serve as cards. One player takes the
license numbers from the first car that passes. The
next player takes the second car's numbers as his cards,
etc., until everyone in the automobile has a hand. If
there are more than five numbers on a license plate,
take the last five; if there are fewer than five on the
license plate, it is rejected and the next car's license is
used. Number one on a license plate is considered the
highest, and is called an Ace. The Zero is next highest
and is called a ten. Obviously there can be no Kings,
Queens, or Jacks. The initials on the license plates do
not count. Hands are rated as in regular poker, in this
sequence of importance: one pair, two pair, three of a
kind, straight, full house, four of a kind and five of a
kind. Five of a kind are better than four of a kind.
(Note: There can be no flush, straight flush, or royal
flush because there are no suits and no pictures.)

11. CONCENTRATION

(For 2 to 4 players)

A deck of cards is spread face down on a table in an irregular pattern. The object of the game is to match these cards in pairs. Player A starts the game by turning two cards face up on the table. If these two cards should happen to be pairs, they become Player A's trick. He takes them and then turns up two other cards. Let us suppose the latter are the ten of spades and Queen of diamonds. As these two cards are not pairs, Player A turns them face down in their original position on the table.

It is now Player B's turn. He exposes one card from any place on the table. Suppose the card Player B turns up is the Queen of spades. Player B remembers that Player A turned up a Queen of diamonds. If player B can locate the Queen of diamonds as his second card to be turned up, he has thus made a pair, and this becomes his trick. If, however, Player B does not find the Queen of diamonds, the two cards he turned up are again placed face down in their original positions on the table. It is now Player C's turn.

Each player may expose only two cards in his turn, unless he has taken a pair, in which case he may have a chance at another pair. The player who takes in the greatest number of pairs wins the game.

A player with a good memory, may take in four, five or even more pairs in one turn, especially toward the end of the game. Remember that the cards must be replaced in the exact position in which they are originally found. Very often a player may be quite positive that he has located a pair, only to be disappointed when a perfectly strange number turns up. This may be a helpful hint to the other players that one of a pair is lurking in the vicinity of the "failure."

12. I PACKED MY BAG

(For 2 or more players)

"I Packed My Bag" may be played by children. The more players, the more difficult the game. The first player starts by saying, "I packed my bag and in it I put (let us suppose) a thimble." The second player continues the game by saying, "'I packed my bag and in it I put a thimble (repeating the previously named article) and a red rose." The third player repeats, "I packed my bag and in it I put a thimble, a red rose, and (then he adds) a lamp shade," and so on around the room. Each player must mention *all* the preceding articles packed in exactly the right order, and then add a new article. Any player who calls off the articles in the wrong order or forgets any one of them drops out of the game. The other contestants continue to call off the old and add a new. The game continues until one player is left—who must necessarily be the winner.

13. BATTLESHIP

(For 2 players)

PLAYER A

WORK SHEET   POSITION OF SHIPS

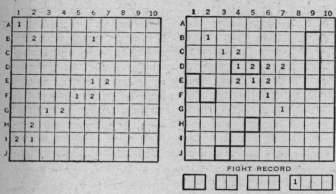

FIGHT RECORD

Each player makes two diagrams as shown, then places in the right-hand diagram four "ships": a battleship of four squares, a cruiser of three, two destroyers of two each (note outlined squares in the diagrams). These ships may be placed in any position you wish—vertically, horizontally or diagonally, but each ship must be made up of connecting squares. Now the shooting begins, with each player trying to sink the other's "ships." At the beginning each player gets six shots. Player A starts, calling for G 3, I 2, E 6, F 5, A 1 and B 6. Player B marks these shots down on his right-hand diagram with the numeral 1 showing on which turn these shots were fired, while Player A marks them as he calls them on his left-hand work sheet also with the numeral 1. After Player A has finished his first turn Player B informs Player A that one of his

PLAYER B

WORK SHEET   POSITION OF SHIPS

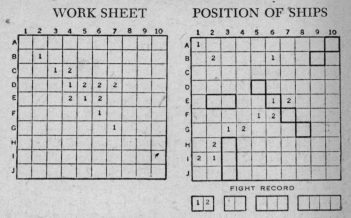

FIGHT RECORD

shots landed on his battleship. Player A then marks the
hit he has scored on the fight record below the large
diagrams. It is now B's turn. His shots are fired at B 2,
C 3, D 4, E 5, F 6, and G 7 and duly marked on his
work sheet. At the end of B's turn, Player A informs
Player B that one of his destroyers has been hit. And
B marks it on his fight record. On A's second turn he
calls for I 1, H 2, G 4, F 6, E 7, and B 2, trying to
locate and sink the battleship which he hit on his first
turn. Player B informs Player A there were "no hits,"
so on Player A's third turn he must still try to find and
sink the rest of the battleship. Player B then calls for
C 4, D 5, D 6, D 7, E 4, E 6. Player A tells Player B
one of his destroyers has been sunk.

Four direct hits sink a battleship, three a cruiser and
two a destroyer. When a player's battleship is sunk he
loses two shots. When a cruiser is sunk he loses two
shots, and one when a destroyer is sunk. Needless to
say, the player who first sinks all of the other player's
ships is declared the winner.

14. SPELLING GAME

(For 12 or more players)

This is an excellent game for children, though adults, including Bing Crosby, Joan Caulfield, Anne Shirley, Fredric March and a host of others enjoyed playing it at a party given by Neysa McMein for the boys who dropped the first atomic bomb.

The game requires a little preparation. You need the following:

1. As many 8 x 10 cards as you have guests. A letter of the alphabet should be painted or drawn clearly on each card.

2. A list of words to be spelled by the group.

The game is played in this manner: Let us suppose you have eighteen guests. Sides are chosen or teams are split up to have the girls against the boys. There must be an equal number on each side, so in this case there would be nine players on each team. Each player is given a card with a letter drawn on it. Each team, however, must have duplicate letters. For example if you give Team A cards with the letters, l, a, s, r, e, v, i, n, u, on them, Team B must also be given cards with l, a, s, r, e, v, i, n, u, on them.

Now, the teams line up opposite each other, with each team member holding a letter card. An adult who serves as referee starts calling out words. For example, in this instance the word might be: *universal*, which uses all of the letters given. Both teams must spell this word out by lining up in the proper order with the letters to spell the word correctly. The team which accomplishes this first, wins one point. The referee marks down the score and another word is called which may be spelled out of the letters written on the cards. Again one point is given to the winning team and so

on until a list of fifteen have been read and scored.
The team with the most points wins the game.

Needless to say, in choosing the letters for the cards,
you should use letters which will give all players a
chance to be used at least once, and if it is possible,
use all of the players at one time at least once. In making up the words to be spelled, you must bear in mind
the age group playing the game, being sure they will
know the words you ask them to spell.

If you have nine players on each team and use the
letters: l, a, s, r, e, v, i, n, u, the following words might
be used for your list:

1	universal	9	slain
2	silver	10	save
3	sliver	11	real
4	alive	12	ruin
5	lane	13	rule
6	sale	14	vile
7	liver	15	nails
8	slave		

15. SCAVENGER HUNT

(For 8 or more players)

A SCAVENGER HUNT is fun especially for teen-
age children. An entire party can be devoted to it.
Any number of children may play. The players are
teamed into pairs. The purpose of the game is for each
team to obtain the objects on a list which is prepared
in advance. The objects are things which are scattered
all over town, and each team is given a copy of the
list. All the players must obtain all the articles on the
prepared list. The team completing the list first and
bringing all of the articles to your house or to an ap-

pointed place wins the game and is given a prize. A list of the following articles is offered as a suggestion:

The Mayor's autograph.

A ticket stub from your local theater.

A box of matches from a local restaurant.

A hair from a horse's tail.

A bottle label from the local pharmacist.

A letterhead from the local mortician.

A bucket of sand (if a beach is nearby) or pebbles from a gravel road.

A registration blank from the local hotel.

An old automobile tire from the local junk pile.

An oyster (if in season).

As you can see, the list is a varied one and in many instances will require ingenuity in the search. Local merchants might be warned beforehand if you have picked their store or theater as a source for some object on the list. It will make it simpler for the players. In order to get all the children back at an appointed time, you might rule that all players return to base with all the objects they have obtained no later than ten o'clock. If no team has completed its list by this time, the team which has obtained the greatest number of the articles is declared the winner.

Answers

1. ALL THE KING'S HORSES

1 and 15: suitcase
2 and 18: lipstick
3 and 8: billboard
4 and 12: chairman
5 and 11: carpet
6 and 20: cowslip
7 and 10: padlock
9 and 19: earnest
13 and 16: pintail
14 and 17: porthole

2. WORD HUNTS

No. 1 Launched

ache	hale
acne	handle
clad	held
clan	lunch
candle	land
cane	lace
caul	lend
dunce	lead
dance	lance
dale	lane
duel	lune
deal	lade
dace	luna
dune	leach
dane	lean
dual	luce
each	nude
elan	nucha
hand	uncle
head	uhlan
haul	ulna
heal	

No. 2 Dynamite

amen	diet	mate	tame
anti	dainty	many	time
amend	daytime	mean	team
admit	dean	meat	tiny
aimed	deity	mind	tain
ament	demit	made	tandem
amid	dent	mane	teind
ante	deny	main	tend
damn	edit	maid	tide
dine	emit	mint	tidy
dime	idea	mend	tinea
dame	idem	name	tine
date	mite	neat	yamen

No. 3 Chorister

core	hector	sire	those
chore	hero	shire	throe
choir	hoist	shore	trice
crest	horse	shot	trio
cite	other	shote	troche
chose	ochre	site	ethics
cost	orris	sect	echo
coster	osier	stir	erst
corset	ostrich	scot	escort
corse	rise	sector	escot
chest	rich	shoe	etch
chit	rice	short	ethos
chorist	recto	sori	
cist	rector	sort	
coir	resort	sortie	
cosher	rest	stoic	
cote	retch	tire	
heir	ichor	tore	
host	itch	tier	
hose	store	torch	
hire	sore	theoric	

3. P. Q. LAR CROSSWORD

Q	Q	Q	Q
U	U	U	U
I	I	I	I
P	P	P	P

4. WORD MAZES

No. 1 General

acre	cheep	die	how
ad	cheer	diet	ide
ade	chop	din	idea
aid	chore	dine	in
alone	chow	drape	inlet
alp	clan	ear	laid
an	cole	earth	lain
and	con	echo	land
ape	cone	end	lane
apt	cop	era	lap
are	core	etch	lead
art	corn	he	leap
cad	cow	head	led
cadet	cowl	heap	lend
cadi	crape	hear	lens
cap	crew	heart	let
cape	crop	hen	letter
caper	crow	help	lone
car	dare	here	lop
card	dart	hoe	lore
care	dear	hole	lorn
caret	dearth	hone	low
carp	den	honey	nap
carpet	deter	hop	near
cart	dial	horn	nee

net par read ten
nether part reap tether
nide per red the
nor pert rein then
now pet rend there
ochre petty rep they
on plaid ret thorn
one plain roe thread
once plan role three
opal plane row trade
or planet rye trap
owe plea said tread
pa plead sale tree
pad plow salon trend
paid pole sand trey
pain pone sane try
pal pony sap wore
pale pore side worn
pan power sin yet
panda pretend snap
pane pretty tear
panel rap teeth

No. 2 Food and Drink

ale ice rye
bass lamb salmon
bean lemon salt
beer malt slaw
beet meal smelt
celery meat tea
cereal oat water
cream rib yams
eels rice yeast

No. 3 Famous People

ADE—George
ABEL—Walter
ALDA—Frances
ALDEN—John
ALLEN—Ethan
BALL—Joseph
BELL—Alexander
BORAH—William
DALE—Esther
DALL—Curtis
DAWES—Charles
DARWIN—Charles
DAWN—Hazel
ELAND—John
ELLIS—Mary
EWING—Thomas
GABLE—Clark
GALE—Zona
GALLI—Aminitore
GARBO—Greta
GHANDI—Mohandas
GOODWIN—Tommy
GRABLE—Betty
GRANDI—Dino
HALE—Nathan
HALL—Jon
HOGAN—Dan
HOOD—Thomas
HOPE—Bob

INGALLS—John
INGE—Dean
LAHR—Bert
LAND—Emery Scott
LANDI—Elissa
LANDIS—James M.
LANDOR—Walter Savage
LANE—Priscilla
LANG—June
LAWES—Lewis E.
LEA—Fanny Heaslip
LELAND—Charles Godfrey
LESLIE—Joan
LEWIS—John L.
LIE—Trygve
LIND—Jennie
LIST—Eugene
NAGEL—Conrad
O'NEILL—Eugene
POE—Edgar Allan
SEWARD—William
STALIN—Joseph
SWING—Raymond
TILDEN—Bill
WARD—Fannie
WEST—Rebecca
WEILL—Kurt
WILDE—Oscar
WISE—Stephen

No. 4 Ready-to-wear Clothes

apron
ascot
cap
cape
chaps
coat
frock

hat
net
rat
sash
scarf
shirt
shoe

shorts
skirt
sock
spats
stock
stocking
tie

5. PERFECT SQUARES

No. 1

C	H	A	N	T
R	U	M	O	R
E	M	P	T	Y
S	O	L	E	S
T	R	Y	S	T

No. 2

S	P	O	R	T
M	O	L	A	R
A	L	I	K	E
R	A	V	E	S
T	R	E	S	S

No. 3

M	A	T	C	H
A	D	I	E	U
R	O	M	A	N
C	R	E	S	T
H	E	R	E	S

No. 4

S	T	A	F	F
C	H	I	L	I
R	O	S	E	S
I	S	L	E	T
M	E	E	T	S

6. HOOK-UP

No. 1

1 thunder
2 storm
3 door
4 man
5 hole
6 out
7 field
8 goal
9 tender
10 foot
11 loose
12 talk
13 fast
14 work
15 horse
16 race
17 riot
18 act
19 up
20 stage
21 entrance
22 gate
23 house
24 mother
25 love
26 life

No. 2

1 red	14 Billy
2 hot	15 goat
3 sun	16 skin
4 dial	17 deep
5 phone	18 sea
6 call	19 side
7 on	20 chair
8 tap	21 leg
9 dance	22 art
10 floor	23 work
11 mop	24 table
12 up	25 cover
13 hill	26 girl

No. 3

1 quick	14 box
2 silver	15 lunch
3 wedding	16 hour
4 ring	17 glass
5 master	18 eye
6 key	19 tooth
7 word	20 brush
8 game	21 off
9 room	22 day
10 rent	23 letter
11 free	24 perfect
12 meal	25 match
13 ticket	26 stick

7. SCRAMBLES

No. 1 Red-Letter Daze

1 Palm Sunday
2 Father's Day
3 New Year's
4 Federal Income Tax
5 Saint Swithin's
6 Armistice Day
7 Lincoln's Birthday
8 Flag Day
9 Election Day
10 Labor Day
11 Christmas
12 Washington's Birthday
13 Independence Day
14 Thanksgiving
15 Saint Valentine's
16 Columbus Day
17 Mother's Day
18 Easter
19 Hallowe'en
20 Memorial Day

No. 2 Books and Authors

1 Sir Walter Scott .... *Ivanhoe*
2 Daphne Du Maurier .... *Rebecca*
3 Herman Melville .... *Moby Dick*
4 Kathleen Winsor .... *Forever Amber*
5 Sinclair Lewis .... *Babbitt*
6 Daniel Defoe .... *Robinson Crusoe*
7 Mark Twain .... *Tom Sawyer*
8 Louisa May Alcott .... *Little Women*
9 Emily Brontë .... *Wuthering Heights*
10 Somerset Maugham .... *Of Human Bondage*
11 Geoffrey Chaucer .... *Canterbury Tales*
12 Charles Dickens .... *David Copperfield*
13 Lloyd Douglas .... *The Robe*
14 Charles Jackson .... *Lost Weekend*
15 Dashiell Hammett .... *The Thin Man*

No. 3 Anniversaries

1st Year	Paper	15th Year	Crystal
2nd Year	Calico	20th Year	China
3rd Year	Muslin	25th Year	Silver
4th Year	Silk	30th Year	Pearl
5th Year	Wood	35th Year	Coral
6th Year	Iron	40th Year	Ruby
7th Year	Copper	45th Year	Sapphire
8th Year	Bronze	50th Year	Gold
9th Year	Pottery	55th Year	Emerald
10th Year	Tin	75th Year	Diamond

8. FAMOUS QUOTATIONS

1 Go west, young man, go west.
2 Don't fire until you can see the whites of their eyes.
3 The only thing we have to fear is fear itself.
4 God helps them that help themselves.
5 I know on which side my bread is buttered.
6 Be good, sweet maid, and let who will be clever.
7 Fools rush in where angels fear to tread.
8 'Tis better to have loved and lost, than never to have loved at all.

9. ANAGRAMS

No. 1 Add One Letter

1 spasm	6 ignorant
2 prophet	7 yachts
3 oyster	8 myriad
4 apart	9 tyrant
5 height	10 anchor

No. 2 Add Two Letters

1 emigrant	6 knight
2 nuisance	7 robust
3 sublime	8 pitcher
4 grimace	9 crystal
5 appeal	10 empty

No. 3 Add Three Letters

1 burlesque	6 romantic
2 influence	7 lecture
3 outline	8 diploma
4 rhapsody	9 catarrh
5 prairie	10 ghetto

10. ADD A LETTER

No. 1	No. 2	No. 3
a	I	a
at	in	at
rat	gin	ate
rate	sing	late
trace	sting	tales
trance	tinges	cleats
certain	glisten	chalets
canister	stealing	satchels
reactions	triangles	matchless
		alchemists

11. GOT YOUR NUMBER

No. 1

23	21	28
29	24	19
20	27	25

No. 3

8	1	6
3	5	7
4	9	2

No. 2

17	24	1	8	15
23	5	7	14	16
4	6	13	20	22
10	12	19	21	3
11	18	25	2	9

No. 4

19	26	3	10	17
25	7	9	16	18
6	8	15	22	24
12	14	21	23	5
13	20	27	4	11

12. THE MISSING VOWEL

A crazy bard, happy as a lark, sat at a bandstand and sang a ballad. A watchman saw a mad chap, angry at grammar and aghast at act, grab a blackjack and start a fracas. Crafty watchman's alarm halts party and madcaps calmly stalk away.

13. WORD PUZZLES

No. 1

1 archway
2 asphyxiate
3 bombshell
4 pachyderm
5 diphtheria
6 Sanskrit
7 rickshaw
8 farmyard
9 tocsin
10 misstep
11 forward
12 anaesthetic
13 glycerine
14 hemorrhage
15 halcyon
16 hamstrung
17 handkerchief
18 asylum
19 rhythm
20 circumvent

No. 2

1 idyll
2 catarrh
3 impromptu
4 abyss   5 fifth
6 distinct   7 jazz
8 satyr   9 disc
10 bankruptcy

No. 3

1 bazaar, or salaam
2 skiing
3 bookkeeper
4 vacuum
5 flivver

No. 4

1 queue
2 aqueous
3 sequoia
4 giaour

No. 5

Each word contains
three letters in their
alphabetical order.

No. 6

1 abstemiously
2 facetiously

No. 7

1 triangle
2 citadel
3 domains
4 agnostic
5 asleep
6 seldom

No. 8

1 real fun
2 best in prayer
3 there we sat
4 rash games in Paris

No. 9

1 underground

No. 10

1 sutler
2 ulster
3 lustre
4 lurest
5 rulest
6 result
7 rustle

No. 11

1 "Have you any eggs?"
2 "Yes, we have eggs."
3 "Have you any ham?"
4 "Yes, we have ham."
5 "O.K., ham and eggs."

14. A GARBLED SPEECH

Now we are engaged in a great civil war, testing whether that nation or any nation, so conceived and so dedicated can long endure.—Lincoln's Gettysburg Address

15. CACHED FOOD

1 okra	7 plum	13 endive	19 beet
2 date	8 orange	14 onion	20 pea
3 olive	9 berry	15 artichoke	21 chard
4 turnip	10 lime	16 spinach	
5 bean	11 potato	17 currant	
6 apple	12 peach	18 pear	

16. MAP OF THE UNITED STATES

1 Maine	25 Illinois
2 New Hampshire	26 Mississippi
3 Vermont	27 Louisiana
4 Massachusetts	28 Arkansas
5 Rhode Island	29 Missouri
6 Connecticut	30 Iowa
7 New York	31 Minnesota
8 New Jersey	32 North Dakota
9 Pennsylvania	33 South Dakota
10 Maryland	34 Nebraska
11 Delaware	35 Kansas
12 Virginia	36 Oklahoma
13 West Virginia	37 Texas
14 North Carolina	38 New Mexico
15 South Carolina	39 Colorado
16 Georgia	40 Wyoming
17 Florida	41 Montana
18 Alabama	42 Idaho
19 Tennessee	43 Utah
20 Kentucky	44 Arizona
21 Ohio	45 California
22 Michigan	46 Nevada
23 Indiana	47 Oregon
24 Wisconsin	48 Washington

17. SYNONYMS

No. 1	No. 2
B	**D**
1 box	1 dash
2 ball	2 deal
3 bat	3 delegate
4 back	4 disorder
5 band	5 draft
6 bag	6 draw
7 bill	7 dress
8 bar	8 drum
9 babble	9 date
10 base	10 deck
11 blow	11 decline
12 blind	12 devil
13 block	13 domestic
14 bluff	14 distemper

18. LITERARY CRYPTS

1 Laws are like cobwebs which catch small flies, but let wasps and hornets break through. —Jonathan Swift

2 To love oneself is the beginning of a life-long romance. —Oscar Wilde

3 The whirligig of time brings in its vengeance. —The Bard

4 A learned blockhead is a greater blockhead than an ignorant one.   —Benjamin Franklin

5 Hatred is the coward's revenge for being intimidated. —G. B. Shaw

6 Nearest the throne itself must be the footstool of humility   —James Montgomery

7 The fox condemns the trap, not himself. —W. Blake

8 In the lexicon of youth—there is no such word as fail. —Bulwer-Lytton

9 That's a valiant flea that dare eat his breakfast on the lip of a lion.   —W. Shakespeare

10 Nothing so needs reforming as other people's habits. —Mark Twain

19. CRAZY CRYPTS

No. 1

Quixotic quack, in quest of quaint quartz, queries querulous quaestor re quality of quartz queen.

No. 2

Muezzin at Egyptian bazaar knocks over knick-knack stand and immediately salaams to Allah.

No. 3

Man murders mother. Alibi: Psychiatrist's diagnosis of oedipus complex.

No. 4

Ghost ghoulishly chases macabre spectre, three sheets to the wind.

No. 5

Crazy cryptographer deciphers Czechoslovakian telegraphy and gets prize as expert linguist.

No. 6

Rhinoceros has tryst with aardvark at zoo, resulting in universal fracas.

20. CODES

No. 1

1

BZM'S. LNNM SNN AQHFGS.

2

3853B54. 25C95M54 4514.

3

XNDYJJS HWANXJWX FSHMTWJI.

No. 2

1 The message read: "Blow up ammunition dumps tonight." It was deciphered by taking the first letter of
   each answer to the definitions and placing them in
   the drawn diagram.

No. 2

1 bouquet	8 male	15 obscure	22 tamper
2 listen	9 maim	16 navy	23 odd
3 omit	10 urn	17 dislike	24 Neptune
4 whiff	11 nap	18 upset	25 illegal
5 use	12 ice	19 mature	26 ghastly
6 poem	13 talk	20 past	27 hammock
7 adult	14 ill	21 sane	28 tar

No. 3 Code Letter

The key to decoding this message lies in the date, July
Fifth. By reading every fifth letter, beginning with the
salutation, the message says:

WATER TOWER ON THAMES TARGET
FOR TWENTIETH.

No. 4 Code Directory

The column of last names starts in each instance with the
letter D, the fourth letter of the alphabet. The fourth letter
in each name, reading down the first column contains part
of the message. The top name in the second column starts
with the letter C, the third letter of the alphabet. The third
letter in each name, in this column, again reading down,
contains the remainder of the message. The message reads:

INTERCEPT PATROL TWENTY
MILES NORTHEAST OF ROUEN

The addresses are merely inserted to make the book look
authentic.

21. WORD PYRAMIDS

No. 1

1 eke
2 edge
3 eagle
4 edible
5 elegize
6 effusive
7 effective
8 effeminate

No. 2

1 R.U.R.
2 Ruhr
3 river
4 rancor
5 realtor
6 reindeer
7 Rochester
8 reconsider
9 regulator
10 register
11 rambler
12 ranger
13 razor
14 rear
15 R.R.R.

No. 3

1 dad
2 dead
3 dread
4 defend
5 descend
6 dividend
7 dachshund
8 dissipated

22. CHANGING WORDS

1 sake, sane, sand, send.
2 say, way, wad, wed, wet.
3 foul, fool, food, fond, find, fine, five.
4 hart, part, port, sort, soft.
5 fist, list, lost, loot, foot, fool, fowl.
6 lone, line, fine, find.
7 heat, beat, boat, boot, foot.
8 wine, wing, sing, song, long.
9 par, far, for, foe.
10 wore, sore, sort, soot, slot, slat, slay, play.

23. FUN WITH WORDS

No. 1

1 resist
2 arrest
3 insert
4 bristle
5 chartreuse
6 pasture
7 description
8 enterprise
9 fluster
10 strike
11 resort
12 scatter
13 respect
14 shorten
15 store

No. 2

1 track
2 arctic
3 crate
4 racket
5 castor
6 caret
7 trance
8 actor
9 carpet
10 chart
11 carrot
12 react
13 cartel
14 carton
15 claret

(24. CONCENTRATION TESTS

No. 1. 17
No. 2. 25
No. 3. 13

No. 4

(1) 24, 192, 768
(2) 8, 23, 47, 68
(3) 2, 8, 6, 12, 9
(4) 12; 240; 10,080; 725,760
(5) 6,048; 1,512; 378

No. 5

(1) 2,100
(2) It is impossible. Traveling up hill at the rate of 15 miles an hour, it took him four minutes to get to the top. In order to average 30 miles an hour for the entire hill, he would have to complete the two miles in four minutes. Obviously, therefore, in this instance he would have to complete the downhill trip in no time at all.
(3) (a) 12 one-cent stamps.
     (b) 12 two-cent stamps.

25. BRAIN PUZZLERS

No. 1 Chain Puzzle

The farmer took the fifth section of three links and cut them into three parts. He inserted them as illustrated, making the cost of cutting and welding two cents each, or six cents all told.

1   2   3

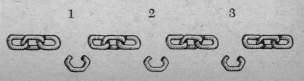

No. 2

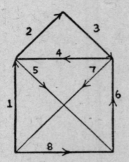

26. FAMOUS "CARS"

1 CARacul
2 CARafe
3 CARamel
4 CARavan
5 CARbon
6 CARbuncle
7 CARcass
8 CARicature
9 CAReer
10 CARess
11 CARnival
12 CARrots
13 CARving
14 CARtograph
15 CARat

27. DOODLES

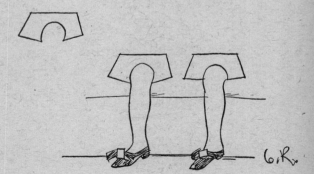

These doodles were drawn from the artist's original lines on page 62 by Ginger Rogers, famous screen star.

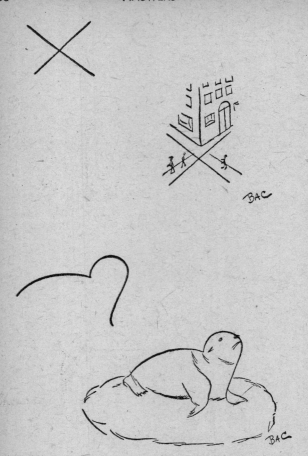

Bennett Cerf, noted publisher and humorist, concocted these doodles from the original lines on page 63.

Danny Kaye, prominent radio, stage and screen comic drew these pictures from the original lines on page 64.

Moss Hart, well known playwright, used the lines on page 65 to make these drawings.

28. DETECT THE M'S

MACHETE
MOTOR
MACKINTOSH JACKET
MAGAZINE
MAID
MAIL
MAINE LICENSE PLATE
MAJOR
MALLARD DUCK
MAN
MANE ON HORSE
MAPLE TREE
MANTILLA
MARE
MARTINGALE HARNESS
MARSHMALLOWS
MATCHES
MATS (PLACE)
MAYONNAISE
MEADOW
MEDICINE
MEERSCHAUM PIPE

MILK
MILL
MINUTE HAND ON
  CLOCK
MOCCASINS
MONASTERY
MONGREL DOG
MONKEY
MONUMENT
MOOSE
MOP
MORNING—INDICATED
  BY CLOCK
MOSQUITO
MOTHER
MOTOR BOAT
MOUNTAIN
MOUTH
MUGS (BEER)
MUSCLES
MUSTACHE
MUSTARD

30. BRIDGE PROBLEMS

No. 1

This hand can be made by a Vienna Coup.

West leads six of hearts. Dummy takes with Jack, and East and South play small. Two of spades is played from Dummy. East wins with his King. His only safe lead is either the Ten of spades or a heart. East plays the Ten of spades, South plays Jack and West the Queen. Dummy's Ace takes the trick. South plays Dummy's Ace of clubs. East, South and West play small clubs. South leads the three of spades from Dummy, East sloughs Five of hearts, South plays nine, West eight. (By playing a small spade from Dummy, South can only lose one spade, no matter which card East plays on first spade trick.) Now South runs his remaining spades, discarding Nine of clubs and Two of diamonds from Dummy. West sloughs the Three of hearts and the Three of clubs, East sloughs the Eight of clubs and Four of diamonds. South then plays his hearts. On the lead of the last heart, East is down to three diamonds to the Queen and Jack, and the King of clubs. If East throws the King of clubs, South's Queen is established for the twelfth trick. If East throws a diamond, North's Jack is established as the twelfth trick.

No. 2

South takes West's lead of the King of diamonds with his Ace, and leads the Ace of clubs. All follow. South now plays the Nine of clubs. West discards the Two of spades, the King of clubs from Dummy, and the Ten is thrown by East. South has seen that the club suit is blocked; and if he runs the clubs, he will only be able to take eight tricks, so he plays the Ten of diamonds from Dummy, throwing West in lead. West plays his remaining three high diamonds, on which South throws a club and a heart, thereby unblocking the club suit and creating five club tricks. The hand *can* be beaten by a double dummy play of West failing to take his high diamonds and leading the Six of spades. But how many players will look a gift horse in the mouth and fail to take their high tricks?

No. 3

This hand can be made by what is commonly called the "smother play." West leads the Ten of spades; South plays the Ace from Dummy; East plays the Nine; and South plays the Four from his own hand. He then plays Ace and King of clubs from Dummy, and trumps the Two of clubs in his own hand. South then plays the Queen and Jack of diamonds. West cannot cover, as he would not make any trump tricks if he did. So he plays two small diamonds. East discards a club on second diamond trick. South then plays Ace of hearts, followed by small heart to Dummy's

King. Queen of hearts is played from Dummy; East and West follow and South discards a spade. Three of hearts is played from Dummy; East discards his last club; South trumps with the Nine of diamonds; and West follows with his last heart. At this stage South leads one of his two losing spade tricks, which East takes with the King. East plays the Queen of spades, which West must win with either the King or Seven of diamonds, and the last trick is won with the Ace of diamonds in Dummy. South has lost only one spade and one diamond trick, thus fulfilling his contract of five diamonds

No. 4

At first glance it is apparent that this is a Dummy reversal problem, which can only be made if the spades are split three and three in the East and West hands. West leads the King of hearts. South wins the trick in Dummy with the Ace of hearts and trumps the Three of hearts with South's Eight of spades. South then leads the Three of diamonds to Dummy's Jack, and trumps the Four of hearts with his Ten of spades. He again leads a small diamond to Dummy's Queen, and trumps the Five of hearts with the Queen of spades. South now leads his only remaining spade, the King, and overtakes it with the Ace in Dummy. The Jack and Nine of spades are led from Dummy, pulling the remaining trumps, and South discards the Two and Four of clubs. Now South's Ace and Ten of diamonds are high, and the Ace and King of clubs take the last tricks for a grand slam.

No. 5

This hand can be made by creating a squeeze on West and several other tricks well known to the experienced bridge player. West leads the Four of clubs; South plays the Eight from Dummy and wins the trick in his own hand with the Queen. He now plays the Six of clubs; West goes in low; and South finesses with the Ten of clubs in Dummy, which holds the trick. East discards the Six of diamonds.

The Ace of spades is played from Dummy. West cannot be kept from holding lead by dropping his King, so plays the Eight, and East and South follow with low spades. South plays the Three of hearts from Dummy. East cannot play Ace, as entire heart suit would be established, so he plays the Two. South plays King, and West the Seven. Now South leads the Nine of spades, West's best defense is to play his King of spades, and South plays Dummy's Five. West's best play is to lead the Queen of hearts, all other hands playing low. West now plays the Jack of spades; South plays the Queen from Dummy and then leads the Thirteenth spade. East plays Seven of diamonds; South Eight of hearts; and West Five of clubs. The Ten of hearts is then played from Dummy, which East must overtake with the Ace. South follows, and West is squeezed. He must protect his club suit, however, so he is forced to throw the Three of diamonds. East leads the Jack of diamonds, and South plays his Two. If West wins the trick with his Ace, he must lead either a club, giving South a finesse through the Ace-Jack, or lead a diamond, putting South in lead in his own hand to take the club finesse. If West ducks the diamond, South wins the trick in Dummy with the Queen and throws West back into lead with another diamond, which he is forced to take, having the Ace alone. West now has only clubs to lead, and Three No Trump is in the bag.

II

1. OBSERVATION QUIZ

1 25
2 Spades and hearts
3 Red
4 Abraham Lincoln
5 There are 42 keys which print letters, numerals or symbols
6 Vertically
7 Below
8 Right

9 Left
10 Alexander Hamilton
11 Red
12 Diamond
13 0   0
    0
  0   0
    0
  0   0
14 On your left
15 Left
16 Right
17 Left
18 Director's name
19 One
20 Four

2. AUTHOR QUIZ

1 Plato
2 Hammett (Dashiell)
3 Chaucer (Geoffrey)
4 Alcott (Louisa May)
5 Hawthorne (Nathaniel)
6 Sherwood (Robert)
7 Parker (Dorothy)
8 James (Henry)
9 Twain (Mark)
10 Carlyle (Thomas)
11 Morley (Christopher)
12 Bacon (Francis)
13 Winsor (Kathleen)
14 Shelley (Percy B.)
15 Cain (James)
16 Cooper (James Fenimore)
17 Hilton (James)
18 Stein (Gertrude)
19 Shaw (George Bernard)
20 Ambler (Eric)
21 Rinehart (Mary Roberts)

22 Wolfe (Thomas)
23 Dumas (Alexander)
24 Voltaire
25 Aesop

3. COMMON DENOMINATOR QUIZ

1 All collaborated with George Kaufman on successful plays.
2 The only vowel is i.
3 All are women who went to battle.
4 They were all [based on] straight plays. *Oklahoma!* was adapted from *Green Grow the Lilacs;* *Carousel* from *Liliom; Going Up* from *The Aviator.*
5 They all were born in Ohio.
6 Women authors using male pseudonyms.
7 They were all Vice Presidents.
8 They are all sweethearts of famous comic-strip characters.
9 They are all historical novels.
10 They were all Vice Presidents who succeeded to the office of the Presidency on the death of their Chief Executives.
11 They wrote the rules for two sports, Queensberry for prize-fighting and Doubleday for baseball.
12 These two men were deaf.
13 They were all assassinated while in office.
14 They all traveled around the world.
15 They were all played by George Arliss in motion pictures.

4. KNOW YOUR ADS?

1 Maxwell House Coffee
2 Packard
3 Gold Seal Flour
4 Old Gold
5 Lucky Strike
6 Coca-Cola
7 American Telephone and Telegraph

8 Ivory Soap
9 Forhan's Toothpaste
10 Paris Garters
11 Calvert Whisky
12 Schlitz Beer
13 Morton Salt
14 Gillette Blade
15 Camay Soap
16 Victor Records
17 Schaefer Beer
18 Fisk Tires
19 Fels-Naphtha Soap
20 Sanka Coffee

5. HOW WELL DO YOU KNOW YOUR ANIMALS?

No. 1

1 From the jackass. Its ears were thought to resemble those of a jackass.

2 By the loose skin above the shoulders with one hand, while supporting the under part of its body with the other. Naturalists say it is painful to a rabbit to lift it by its ears.

3 No. They subsist entirely on a vegetable diet consisting of bark and tender shoots.

4 No. Many of the New World monkeys grasp and climb with their tails, but no Old World monkey has ever been seen employing his tail as a "fifth hand."

5 When an elephant lies down it stretches its hind legs backward and the front legs forward.

6 No. A camel's backbone is as straight as any other four-legged animal's. The hump consists of fatty tissue.

7 As a cow eats, the food is not at first thoroughly chewed. Later the undigested food is regurgitated and chewed again. This returned food in the cow's mouth is called the cud.

8 Yes. Principally through the soles of their feet, where the largest sweat glands are located.

9 Through breeding zebras it has been learned that the zebra is a light-brown animal with black or dark brown stripes.
10 They rise hind legs first.

No. 2

1 colony	16 herd	32 chick
2 sloth	17 pack	33 fawn
3 hive or colony	18 sow	34 puppy
4 herd	19 doe	35 duckling
5 herd	20 cow	36 calf
6 school or shoal	21 duck	37 tadpole
7 flock or gaggle	22 vixen	38 gosling
8 brood	23 goose	39 pullet
9 pack	24 lioness	40 colt or foal
10 pride	25 ewe	41 cub
11 bevy	26 mare	42 lamb
12 muster	27 hind	43 cygnet
13 nide	28 tigress	44 shoat
14 covey	29 cub	45 calf
15 bevy	30 bullock	46 parr
	31 heifer	

6. MYTHICAL CITIES

1 Ill.	13 Tenn.
2 Mo.	14 Del.
3 Wy.	15 Mass.
4 Tex.	16 Ore.
5 Ala.	17 Minn.
6 Conn.	18 Ga.
7 La.	19 Pa.
8 Wash.	20 Me.
9 Ark.	21 Mich.
10 Miss.	22 Kan.
11 Ky.	23 N. C.
12 Cal.	

7. IT'S ALL ENGLISH

1 Radio
2 Elevator
3 Trolley car
4 run in stocking
5 Policeman
6 Saloon
7 Billboard
8 Gasoline
9 Two weeks
10 Men's garters
11 Freight cars
12 Tracks
13 Setting-up exercises
14 Court
15 Line of people waiting their turn

8. SPELLING TEST

No. 1

1 churches
2 elves
3 forgoes
4 echoes
5 armies
6 feet
7 gases
8 ladies
9 hobos, or hoboes
10 knives
11 radios
12 tangos
13 mercies
14 lives
15 mice
16 mottoes, or mottos
17 keys
18 selves
19 men
20 maestros
21 potatoes
22 porticoes, or porticos
23 cameos
24 folios
25 cargoes, or cargos

9. TEST YOUR GRAMMAR

1 going
2 which
3 were
4 take
5 bring
6 shall
7 is
8 whoever
9 may
10 he
11 chooses

10. PICK THE CORRECT DEFINITION

1 profit
2 native
3 flowing
4 diverse
5 draw
6 soften by soaking
7 improve

8 beat
9 fallacy
10 a little
11 unwholesome
12 outweigh
13 terse
14 insinuation

11. CHOICE TEST

1 (a) Magnetic iron ore
2 (c) 21
3 (c) Charles L. McNary
4 (b) Lewis Carroll
5 (b) Faneuil Hall
6 (a) Lake Michigan
7 (b) 1902
8 (b) John Hancock
9 (a) Edgar Lee Masters
10 (c) Jane Addams
11 (c) Catherine of Aragon
12 (b) Greece
13 (a) Taft
14 (a) London
15 (b) Jupiter

12. TRUE OR FALSE

No. 1

1 TRUE. Cream is lighter because of the fat and oil content.
2 TRUE. His real name was François Marie Arouet.
3 FALSE. It is in France, in the province of Haute Savoie.
4 FALSE. They grow less than the rest of the body, because they are longer, proportionally, at birth, but they do grow.
5 FALSE. They belong to entirely different branches of the order known as rodents.

6 TRUE.   Los Angeles is a seaport, with its harbor on San Pedro Bay.

7 TRUE.   Driving very quickly consumes extra gasoline.

8 FALSE.   It was named after King Edward the Seventh, formerly Albert, Prince of Wales.

9 FALSE.   A simple fracture may be a fracture of one or many bones, but the skin remains unbroken, while a compound fracture means that the skin is broken.

10 FALSE. It was named after the coffee house where the marine underwriters first met.

11 FALSE. He was born with a withered arm.

12 TRUE.   Diamonds will burn if heated sufficiently.

13 FALSE. The male mosquito does not bite.

14 FALSE. There is no verification of this common belief.

15 FALSE. 1932 was a leap year but 1900 was not. Every year divisible by four is a leap year, except those divisible by 100 and not by four hundred.

16 FALSE. A toad molts and eats its own skin, but not a snake.

17 FALSE. Florida has the longest coastline.

18 FALSE. Boxing day, an English holiday, is the day after Christmas, when the boxes left in the church are opened and distributed.

19 TRUE.   It is the very first stage in the training of a printer.

20 TRUE.   No citizen, naturalized or natural born, is subject to the immigration laws.

No. 2

1 TRUE.   Actually, the Arctic is dry, and there is very little snow there.

2 TRUE.   A person is not likely to sink much below the armpits, unless he struggles to get out of the quicksand.

3 FALSE.   In the first ten years following its erection the mast on top of the Empire State Building was struck by lightning sixty-eight times.

4 TRUE.   Those who train homing pigeons claim they have to be taught.

5 FALSE.   Vilhjalmur Stefansson, author of *Adventure in Error*, has seen thousands of wolves in their natural state. He says that he has never seen any aggregate of wolves in close association larger than the parents and cubs of one family.

6 TRUE.   The bat is guided by the echo of myriads of tiny squeaks that it sends out continuously while in flight, squeaks that bounce off obstacles and return in time to warn it to alter its course.

7 FALSE.   Science has proven that bees do not die after stinging, thus disproving the commonly believed theory.

8 FALSE.   Rigor mortis sets in gradually, from three to five hours after death, lasts (usually) from twelve to twenty-four hours, and then gradually fades away, leaving the body limp again.

9 FALSE.   Drowned women and drowned men have been found both face upwards and face downwards.

10 TRUE.   It gets colder in Montana, by as much as ten degrees than it ever does at the North Pole.

13. LITERARY QUIZ

1 Henry James.
2 Geoffrey Chaucer.
3 (a) *Silas Marner* by George Eliot.
  (b) *The Rivals* by Richard Sheridan.
  (c) *Twelfth Night* by Shakespeare.
  (d) *The Old Curiosity Shop* by Charles Dickens.
4 *The Merchant of Venice, The Tempest, Two Gentlemen of Verona, Much Ado About Nothing, Twelfth Night.*
5 Scheherazade.
6 "Barkis is willing."
7 Charles Reade.

8 Catastrophe, locality, and day. These are Aristotle's
   unities of time, place, and action.
9 (a) Pythias, (b) Chloe, (c) Joan.
10 Battle of Hastings.
11 A siege or seat at the round table which was reserved
   for him who achieved the quest of the Holy Grail. It
   subsequently bore the name of Sir Galahad.
12 Charles Lamb.
13 A stock company of nearly seventy members among
   whom were Hawthorne, Charles Dana, and Margaret
   Fuller. Although it was not a financial success and
   only lasted five years, it was important in its intel-
   lectual results.
14 John Milton.
15 Sancho Panza.

14. QUIZ ON WORLD WAR II

1 August 6, 1945.
2 September 3, 1939.
3 Graf Spee.
4 June 14, 1940.
5 Saburo Kurusu and Admiral Nomura.
6 June 22, 1941.
7 *Prince of Wales* and *Repulse*.
8 May 6, 1942. Lieutenant General Jonathan Wainwright.
9 Lidice.
10 Admiral Jean Darlan.
11 Pietro Badoglio.
12 June 5, 1944.
13 Dumbarton Oaks in Washington, D.C.
14 May 6, 1945.
15 August 14, 1945.

15. SCIENCE QUIZ

1 Nitrogen, oxygen, argon, carbon dioxide, hydrogen, and
   water vapor.
2 The Aurora Borealis is believed to be the result of a
   discharge of electricity through the thin atmosphere
   in a region fifty to a hundred miles above the earth.

3 Deserts are caused by: prevalence of dry winds; separation from the sea by mountain barriers; their great distance from oceans or other areas of evaporation.

4 West Indies and China Sea.

5 Unlike most substances, water is lighter in the solid than in the liquid state.

6 39 degrees Fahrenheit.

7 Rainbows are caused by the reflection and refraction of sunlight in drops of rain.

8 Stalactites hang from the roofs of caves; stalagmites rise from the floors of caves.

9 Metals, gas, carbon, wet earth, and water containing salts and acids.

10 They prevent fires. When the flow of electricity increases beyond its limit, the fuse melts and breaks the circuit.

11 Water will boil sooner in a polished kettle. A dull surface radiates heat twenty times faster than a polished surface.

12 A body will weigh more at either pole than at the equator. This is due to the fact that the centrifugal force is greater at the equator and that the equator is farther from the earth's center. This diminishes the force of gravity.

13 It is the distance that light travels in a year, and is used to compute the distance between the earth and the stars. One light year is almost six trillion miles.

14 The Zodiac is a zone of the heavens, within which lie the paths of the sun, moon and principal planets.

15 Corundum.

16. GEOGRAPHICAL QUIZ

1 Dover, Delaware
  Indianapolis, Indiana
  Oklahoma City, Oklahoma

2 Augusta, Maine
  Albany, New York

Atlanta, Georgia
Austin, Texas
Annapolis, Maryland

3 Highways running from north to south bear odd numbers, and United States highways running from east
   to west bear even numbers.

4 Captain Cook, an English navigator, explored widely
   in the Pacific Ocean, adding Hawaii and numerous
   other islands to the known world.
   Vasco da Gama reached India in 1497.
   Peary raised the American flag over the North Pole on
   April 17, 1909.

5 The land mass of the Western Hemisphere, with its ad-
   jacent islands, is called America. The name was given
   in honor of Amerigo Vespucci, an Italian navigator,
   who is said to have visited South America in 1499.

6 Crater Lake: Southwestern Oregon
  Glacier: Northwestern Montana
  Lassen Volcanic: Northern California
  Rocky Mountain: North Middle Colorado
  Mount Rainier: West Central Washington
  Sequoia: California
  Yellowstone: Wyoming, Montana and Idaho

7 Maine, New Hampshire, Vermont, Massachusetts,
   Rhode Island and Connecticut.

8 Canada is larger than the United States, excluding
   Alaska.

9 The official U.S. Census in 1940 was: 7,454,995.

10 Russia. It was bought in 1867. We paid $7,200,000.

11 1 Mexico City .... Moscow
   2 Montreal .... Munich
   3 Montevideo .... Manchester
   4 Melbourne .... Marseilles
   5 Mukden .... Madrid
   6 Madras .... Milan

12 The original thirteen, Texas and Oklahoma. All other
    States were territories before they were admitted to
    the Union.

13 1 New Hampshire   8 Delaware
   2 Massachusetts   9 Maryland
   3 Rhode Island   10 Virginia
   4 Connecticut   11 South Carolina
   5 New York   12 Georgia
   6 New Jersey   13 North Carolina
   7 Pennsylvania
14 Missouri-Mississippi, Nile and Amazon. (They are about 4,000 miles long.)
15 Oklahoma.
16 Portland, Oregon.
17 Maine.
18 Between Utah, Colorado, Arizona and New Mexico.
19 Arizona.
20 Canberra.

17. MUSICAL QUIZ

1 Mozart.
2 Cole Porter. *Boola, Boola.*
3 Johannes Brahms.
4 *Lead, Kindly Light.*
5 *The Lost Chord.*
6 *The King's Henchman.*
7 Piano.
8 *Hänsel and Gretel.*
9 Chamber music is intimate music, usually written for string instruments, to be performed as duets, trios, quartets, quintets and the like, frequently with additional instruments such as the piano or clarinet.
10 J. S. Bach.

18. MATHEMATICAL QUIZ

1 A unit is one, or a single thing. One day, one dollar.
2 A factor is any of the numbers which, when multiplied together form a product. 8 and 3 are factors of 24. 2 and 4 are factors of 8.
3 Addends are numbers to be added.

4 3/4.
5 50/3.
6 1-5/12.
7 When the process of division is carried out in full with
   every step written down, it is called long division.
   When the multiplication and subtraction in the process
   of division are performed mentally, only the quo-
   tient figures and the differences being written at each
   step, it is called short division.

8

9 $20.
10 25 per cent.

19. GENERAL QUIZ

1 No.
2 Gouverneur Morris, in 1782. He was then assistant to
   Superintendent of Finance Robert Morris.
3 When booze was sold to Indians, the peddlers carried
   the firewater in their boots to hide it from govern-
   ment officials.
4 None. It is made of copper, nickel and zinc.
5 Bucket shop is the popular name of the office of a
   broker who is not a member of the official Stock
   Exchange.
6 At the foot of Pompey's statue in the Senate house in
   Rome.
7 "Neither snow, nor rain, nor heat, nor gloom of night
   stays these couriers from the swift completion of
   their appointed rounds." Herodotus.
8 The Danish flag.

9 The barber pole is a relic of the days when barbers were also surgeons. Few people could read and pictures and emblems were used as shop signs. The emblem of the profession was a spirally painted white and red pole. The white ground represented the bandages used and the red stripe represented the blood.

10 Queen Berengaria, wife of Richard the Lionhearted.

V

1. PIN THE TAIL ON THE ANIMAL

1 b	4 e
2 f	5 c
3 a	6 d

BANTAM BOOKS

The famous mysteries, novels and books of humor, cartoons and non-fiction listed here are all available through the dealer from whom this Bantam Book was purchased.

Bantam Books, Inc., 1107 Broadway, N. Y. 10, N. Y.